IS THERE ANYBODY OUT THERE?

DARA ✦ BRIAIN

Illustrated by
Luna Valentine

Scholastic Children's Books,
Euston House, 24 Eversholt Street,
London NW1 1DB, UK

A division of Scholastic Ltd
London ~ New York ~ Toronto ~ Sydney ~ Auckland
Mexico City ~ New Delhi ~ Hong Kong

Published in the UK by Scholastic Ltd, 2020

ISBN 978 07023 0394 4

Printed and bound by Bell & Bain Limited

2 4 6 8 10 9 7 5 3

Papers used by Scholastic Children's Books
are made from wood grown in
sustainable forests.

IS THERE ANYBODY OUT THERE?

DARA ⬢ BRIAIN

Illustrated by Luna Valentine

SCHOLASTIC

Dedicated to the people of TripleyMary. May your three suns always shine brightly and, next time, may you get to decide what your planet is called.

CONTENTS

IS ANYBODY OUT THERE?

When you look up at the night sky, and see the **THOUSANDS** of twinkling lights from stars dotted throughout the Universe, do you ever think to yourself, I wonder, while I'm looking up there, is anyone looking back at me?

Are they sitting in their garden, also looking up at their constellations, their

solar system

and neighbouring planets, and picking out a faintly twinkling light, that has travelled all the way from our Sun, and wondering who lives round **THAT STAR?**

12

How do we know that every star we look at
isn't surrounded by planets just like **EARTH**,
filled with Earth-like animals and Earth-like people,
asking Earth-like questions about us on EARTH?

And if they are out there, what is their planet like?
What kind of **CREATURES** are they? Can we go
and visit them?

And if we could go and visit them, how long
would that take? And what kind of ship
would we travel in?

**And why are there so many
questions?** Surely the whole book isn't just
going to be *QUESTION* after *QUESTION* after *QUESTION?*
Surely there must be some answers at some stage?
Surely I can start a single sentence in this
book in a normal voice before realizing
halfway through that I have to do a

"**QUESTIONS**" voice and I'm doing that now and my voice is just getting **higher** and **higher** and where is the question mark, oh thank heavens, here it is: ❓

Yes, there will be questions, because this is one of the greatest questions that we have ever asked as a thinking animal. **Are we alone, or is there any other form of intelligent life out there?**

But we will also have some answers! They'll start on the very next page. We'll learn how the **Solar System** started, how life started on **EARTH**, where to find other planets just like this one, and how to send them **A GREETINGS CARD**.

On the way, we'll meet **pulsing stars**, and tiny bears living on the **MOON**, and planets with four stars in the sky, and the **SMARTEST OCTOPUS** in the world.

But more **EXCITINGLY**, there will be lots of questions we don't have answers for yet, lots of problems we're only just working out how to solve, and lots and **lots of distant worlds** we're only just discovering.

And we'll end up back with the **FIRST QUESTION** we started out with: is somebody, or something, looking right back at you from space? And when we look up at the stars, in which direction should we wave, to say

"HELLO?"

A month until the science fair...

NOBODY HAS EVER MET AN ALIEN.

We have **no idea** where they might live, or what their home planet might be like. We have **no idea** what they might look like or how they might live. So, you probably think that writing an

ENTIRE BOOK

about them would be pure guesswork. And yes, it is. **But** it is the type of guesswork that scientists and thinkers have been engaged in for **THOUSANDS OF YEARS**. As far back as the second century AD, the Assyrian writer Lucian wrote of a journey to the **Moon**, which he found populated by three-headed vultures, **mosquitos the size of elephants** and women who were part grapevine, so that if you kissed them you would end up drunk.

Since we can see it easily and often, the **Moon** is an obvious candidate for wonderment, but most of the **planets** in our **SOLAR SYSTEM**, or at least the ones visible to the naked eye (Mercury, Venus, Mars, Jupiter and Saturn), have been known about for as long as most things have been known about. It's not surprising they got noticed really. Even though they are up in the sky with the stars, **they don't behave like stars**.

STARS

sit in their regular constellations, year in, year out, rotating around the sky, pretending to be dogs or warriors or snakes or all that **constellations** stuff. Occasionally (very occasionally, maybe once every 300 years) one of the stars we can see from Earth will go **SUPERNOVA**, where it runs out of fuel, collapses and explodes, much like a small child who is eating sweets, but then runs out of sweets, collapses and explodes. The supernova makes the star **SHINE** very brightly for a period of weeks or months and then fall back into darkness, either as a very heavy and dense **NEUTRON STAR** or, if it's really big, as a **black hole**. Maybe I should tell you more about supernovas later. They're pretty great.

Generally though, when they aren't **EXPLODING**, stars behave in a fairly regular way.

The **PLANETS** in our Solar System, on the other hand, are in their own orbits around the **SUN**, and we get closer to and further away from them all the time, which means to our eyes they seem to wander **in** and **out** of sight along the lower part of the sky. In fact, their name comes from the Greek word "**planetes**", which means "**wanderer**". Astronomers spotted these planets and were led to wonder if they, like Earth,

supported life. Sometimes though, the **faint** images they could see by squinting at the sky, or later, **squinting** through their **telescopes**, were less helpful than you'd hope in finding answers to this **huge** question.

THE CANALS OF MARS

In 1877, the Italian astronomer Giovanni Schiaperelli (say that ten times fast) mapped **Mars** through his telescope and noted dark lines spreading across the planet, which he termed "channels" or in Italian, *canali*. This then got wrongly translated into English as "canals" and a **huge fuss erupted**, based around one idea: if there are canals, then they must have been constructed, like the canals on Earth. So who made them? `It must be aliens!`

The canals on Mars made people lose sense completely. The amateur astronomer Percival Lovell

built his own observatory, drew maps of Mars covered in canals, gave **popular lectures** and wrote **three** books about the planet with detailed explanations of his theory that Mars was running out of water and had to use the canals to bring **WATER** from melting snow at the poles to the equator to keep Martians alive. Of course, it doesn't matter how good your **telescope** is, it is **really, really difficult** to get a clear view of the surface of Mars, and the **DRAWINGS** were made from memory, sketched from glimpses of the surface, then later joined together. And once the idea had been put in people's heads, **they began to see what they wanted to see.**

MARS BOATING HOLIDAYS

The ability to see things from and in space is often overstated. Here is a great "Catch out an adult!" moment. Ask a grown-up what is the only human-made thing that can be seen from the Moon and they will go, "**Aha! The Great Wall of China!**", because that is what they have always been told, and it sounds pretty cool. **It's not true**, of course, as many astronauts have confirmed. Perhaps from a very low orbit, if the conditions are just right, but not from anywhere in space proper. And to see the Great Wall of China from the Moon, as the popular myth has it, would require human eyesight to be **17,000 times** better than it is. The human-made objects that can be most easily seen from the **International Space Station (ISS)** are the Earth's cities, of course, particularly at night when they are lit up.

If, however, your mother, say, was an astronaut on the Space Station and you wanted to write "**I love you, Mum**" on the ground so that she could see it with the naked eye as she flew over, the letters would have to be two kilometres (km) high. **Send her a text instead. They get great internet coverage on the Space Station.**

The "canals on Mars" idea lasted only until people started taking photographs of the planet rather than sketching. Nonetheless, the idea of Martians as our most likely candidates for alien buddies, rather than **VENUSIANS** or **SATURNIANS**, had taken hold.

And then the **FLYING SAUCERS** appeared...

WHAT'S THAT IN THE SKY?

During the 1950s and 1960s there was a sudden boom in sightings of possible alien invaders. The term **"flying saucer"** is thought to have been the fault of one man, Kenneth Arnold, a businessman in America who claimed to have seen a number of alien spacecraft in the Cascade Mountains, in Washington State. He said they were **"LIKE A SAUCER IF YOU SKIPPED IT ACROSS WATER"**.

Presumably he was explaining the way in which they flew, but the name "flying saucer" stuck and for a couple of decades the world was obsessed with **fuzzy photographs** of saucers, triangles and cigars, all apparently arrived from distant planets. Many of the sightings were of prototype military aircraft like the triangular **"Stealth" bomber** launched by the Americans in the 1980s. Some were clearly unusual cloud formations or weather balloons, and some were just **TERRIBLE** photographs.

Of course, we can't say for definite that aliens haven't visited here in saucers, but for the last twenty years or so, almost the **ENTIRE POPULATION** of the world has been carrying cameras around in its pockets all the time, and yet the supply of **fuzzy** images of alien spaceships has dried up almost completely. **Maybe aliens are just more private than we imagined?**

But where were the scientists during all this? While the world was convulsed with excitement at fuzzy pictures of strange **cloud formations** and convincing themselves that we were regularly being visited by **EXTRA-TERRESTRIALS?**

Where were the scientists when the world needed them?

NO PHOTOS, PLEASE!

Well, they were at lunch, of course.

VERY CLEVER PARADOX

During the Second World War, while trying to master **nuclear power**, a number of labs were created in America to bring together some very, very clever people to share their research. Among them was the man who created the very first ever nuclear reactor – a very, very, very clever man called Enrico Fermi. He is the father of the famous **FERMI PARADOX**. A paradox is an idea that sounds clever, but when you think about, ends up revealing itself to be **untrue**.

One day, while at lunch with his colleagues, the conversation was about **HIGH-SPEED SPACE TRAVEL**. This was a conversation between very, very clever people, but it is only remembered for what Fermi said, because he was very, very, **very clever** and so the thing he said was cleverer than what everyone else said, by about one "very". And like a lot of very, very, very clever things people have said throughout history, it was **very, very, very clever** because it was very, very, very simple. Midway through the conversation, as they discussed whether faster-than-light travel could ever be achieved, Fermi suddenly shouted, "**But where are they?**" And that was it. That was the **very, very, very clever thing**.

You should try **SHOUTING** it next time you're having lunch and see if they name a paradox after you.

"Would you like some more chips, dear?"

"**BUT WHERE ARE THEY?**"

"They're on the table, in front of you…"

(Although, that isn't a bad paradox. To want chips so much you can't even see them right in front of you…)

Here's why Fermi's remark became famous. He summed up the entire argument against the existence of alien life. When he said, "But where are they?" he was saying: there are **BILLIONS** of stars in the Milky Way. If they formed the way our Sun did, as we expect, some of them probably have an Earth-like planet. Multiply "some" by billions of stars and that should mean a lot of Earth-like planets. These planets have been around for a **Long time**, so there's a good chance that life will have evolved the same as it did here, maybe slower, maybe **faster**. On Earth, we're beginning to develop the technology to travel across space, so if any of those more-developed societies on these many Earth-like planets have done the same, they've had plenty of time to criss-cross the galaxy and arrive here.

SO, WHERE ARE THEY?

Here's a way to make your brain spin: it's not unlike the idea that we'll never discover time travel. Here's why: if, at some point, time travel is invented, wouldn't there be tourists? But **NOBODY** has ever met a time-traveller. We'd have noticed. That would be pretty big news. Since we've never met a time-traveller, it must mean that it will **NEVER** be invented. (Here's brain spin two: it may just mean it isn't possible to go BACK in time. But we might able to go FORWARD.)

Fermi's paradox is interesting because it tried to balance the **VERY BIG NUMBERS** (the stars in the Solar System) **AGAINST THE VERY SMALL NUMBERS** (the chances that life has evolved on another planet). Since we don't keep meeting aliens or finding their **SPACESHIPS** when we dig up **DINOSAUR BONES**, it would seem the **SMALL NUMBERS WIN**. That's to say that the chances of life just appearing on a random planet is a much smaller number than we thought, which is sad.

Another example of this way of thinking is **Drake's equation**, named after the astronomer **Frank Drake**, who tried to work out the chances of us ever finding **INTELLIGENT LIFE**. **Again, you take all the big numbers** (billions of stars multiplied by how many planets we think are around each star, multiplied by the billions of years in the age of the Universe) and weigh them up against all the little **numbers** (the chance of life appearing, multiplied by the chances of it being intelligent life, multiplied by the chances of that intelligent life inventing **SPACESHIPS**

or **RADIO** broadcasting or something else we might notice). It's a clever way to break down a huge question into a series of steps, each of which is worth investigating on its own. If we're lucky, the **big numbers** outweigh the small ones and the chances of finding life are high. And, if you're really lucky, they name the equation after you.

(If you want your own **equation** – and who wouldn't? – **why not just try multiplying big versus small**? For example, how much you would like some sweets right now **[BIG NUMBER]** multiplied by how many sweets you will eat if you are given the chance [very big number] – all of that weighed against **A REALLY SMALL NUMBER**, like, the chances that if you asked your mum or dad, or headteacher, say, that they would give you those sweets right now. Often the number is quite different for your mum or dad, and generally incredibly low for your headteacher – try it, next you see them. Say, "**GIVE ME SOME SWEETS!**" and see what you get for it.)

LISTENING FOR LIFE

Frank Drake did more than devise an equation; he came up with a way of searching for alien life. Spaceships are not the only way to send ourselves out into the Universe. **Every radio or television programme we broadcast heads out from our planet into space.** Radio waves are a form of what we call electromagnetic radiation, which is a fancy word for all the different types of light, including all the types of light you can't see. All light, and radio waves, microwaves, X-rays and loads more, are carried by **ENERGY WOBBLING** in the electric and magnetic fields that exist all around us at all times. This can be a strange concept to get your head around (there's a lot more explaining of it in one of my other books, *Secret Science*) but

you'll be relieved you only need
to know two things right now:

**Radio waves travel at the speed
of light, so: very fast, and ...**

**They can be "seen" by the
right kind of telescope.**

This all means that, since radio stations began to
become widespread in the 1920s, we have been
sending our radio programmes, and later, television
programmes, out into space, and now those original
broadcasts will have travelled **100 LIGHT YEARS** away.

There are just over 500 Sun-like stars within 100
light years of Earth, and about 14,000 other stars of
different types. So among those solar systems, is there
a planet listening in to our old radio programmes, like
a giant, interstellar version of Classic Hits radio?

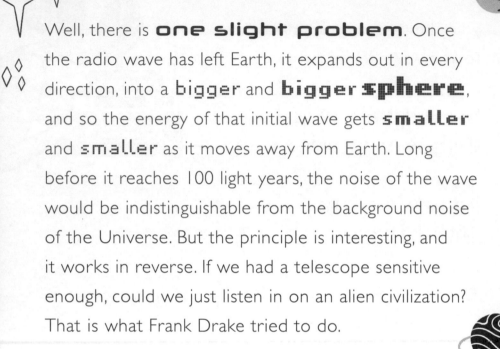

Well, there is **one slight problem**. Once the radio wave has left Earth, it expands out in every direction, into a **bigger** and **bigger sphere**, and so the energy of that initial wave gets **smaller** and **smaller** as it moves away from Earth. Long before it reaches 100 light years, the noise of the wave would be indistinguishable from the background noise of the Universe. But the principle is interesting, and it works in reverse. If we had a telescope sensitive enough, could we just listen in on an alien civilization? That is what Frank Drake tried to do.

In 1960, he bagged some time on a **PRETTY HUGE TELESCOPE** in the Green Bank Observatory in West Virginia, United States. He pointed it at the nearby Sun-like stars of Tau Ceti (11.9 light years away) and Epsilon Eridani (10.5 light years away), calculating that he just might be able to pick up the distant sounds of a civilization. Although this effort didn't yield any definite answers, Drake went on to found the Search for Extra-

Terrestrial Intelligence (SETI) and the organization now uses telescopes to survey the skies from Argentina, Australia and the United States. They search not only for radio broadcasts but also for laser pulses and, while the sky may be huge, they are seeking to narrow down the search as we learn more not just about distant stars, but for the first time ever, about the planets that orbit them.

Hey, are you using that telescope right now?

For years, SETI has worked by "borrowing" time on other people's radio telescopes (like having a go on somebody else's cool bike when they aren't using it) and choosing narrow sections of the skies to point at. They have heard nothing conclusive yet, but the search is getting bigger. SETI recently announced that, thanks to a **huge donation** from Paul Allen, the co-founder of the software company Microsoft, **they have built their own array of dedicated telescopes**, allowing them to expand the search from **1,000 stars to a million** over the next twenty years.

So, is this the way we discover alien life? The equivalent of **CUPPING YOUR EAR AT THE SKY** is certainly a lot cheaper than getting in a rocket and flying hundreds of light years.

Sometimes though, when you listen really closely to space, you can discover something even more unexpected than aliens…

LITTLE GREEN MEN?

In 1967, scientists and students from Cambridge University built a large but rudimentary radio telescope in a field, using poles and wire. They were scanning the skies for the flickering radio signals of distant objects, when one of the students, Jocelyn Bell (now called **DAME JOCELYN BELL BURNELL**, so – spoiler alert – she's about to do something pretty amazing and historic) noticed that there was one signal that was pulsing with an almost mechanical regularity. On it would flash every `1.3 seconds`, then off, then back on again after another `1.3 seconds`. This kind of regularity is very odd when looking at the natural background noise of space, so strange in fact that Jocelyn and her professor gave it the joking name

"**LGM-1**", which stood for **LITTLE GREEN MEN**. Surely only a broadcast from an alien race would send such a regular beam?

Meetings were held in the university about what to do with this signal, with some professors even suggesting dumping the data rather than inviting the **FUSS** it would cause by announcing that they had found alien life. Jocelyn did what any good scientist does, though, and went back to the data. Examining it closely, she found that there was another, similar signal coming from a different part of space, but this time every **1.5 seconds**. There was no chance of there being two entirely different, distant civilizations signalling Earth in the exact same way. The scientists must have discovered A NEW NATURAL PHENOMENON instead.

What they had found are **pulsars**: stars that have burned through all their fuel and collapsed into **NEUTRON** stars, stars so incredibly dense that a single teaspoon of their matter would weigh the same as a city on Earth. Pulsars are **extra exciting** though because they begin to rotate when they collapse and send huge beams

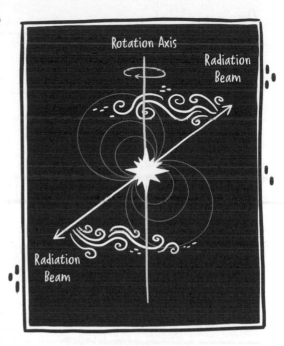

of radio waves off into the Universe. **From where we sit, it's like watching a lighthouse.** The beam of radio waves passes, flashes at us and moves on, so it is as if the pulsar is **flashing on and off**. Pulsars are so regular, they can be used as astronomical clocks, and so identifiable, they might one day be used as navigation beacons for interstellar travel. **Jocelyn may not have discovered aliens, but she might have discovered the map of the Universe instead.** Not bad for someone working out in a field.

OH, SO YOU
WANT TO MEET
ALIENS?

HOW DO YOU BUILD A PLANET?

Searching for alien life is **a big job** and it involves looking across an entire Universe. To make it a tiny bit easier, let's try, like great scientists do, to break **a really big problem down** into a number of slightly smaller problems and see if we can solve those instead.

Let's work out, for example, where we need to look. **Where in the Universe would we find life?**

WELL ... HERE, FOR A START - **ON EARTH.**

Life has done pretty well on Earth, as you'll probably have noticed if you've ever been stuck in traffic on the way to school. Or if you've ever lifted a stone and seen all the insects **scurrying** around. There is a lot of life on Earth. Maybe there is something in how life started here that will help us when it comes to finding those **EXTRA-TERRESTRIALS**.

So let's have a **zip** through the history of life on Earth, starting before life was even here. Starting before Earth was even here, actually.

After all, life needs somewhere to live, so the first thing we have to work out is: **how do we build a planet?**

We'll need a star to go alongside our new planet, for a bit of energy, but luckily for us, planets and stars are both made from the same thing: a **simple, huge, cloud** of **gas** and **dust**. Yes, dust. Run your finger along the highest shelf you can reach. What did you find? Dust, and without it we wouldn't be here. **THAT'S HOW THE STORY OF LIFE BEGINS.**

You see, space isn't quite as **empty** as the name "space" would seem to imply.

At the start was the **BIG BANG**, when space **expanded** into existence, and the very basic bits of everything were swirling around, and probably blinking in shock at how quickly it had happened. Eventually though (after about 380,000 years) it all cooled down enough, and things stopped 𝓑𝓞𝓤𝓝𝓒𝓘𝓝𝓖 off each other enough, so that the **electrons**, **protons** and **neutrons**, the bits that everything is made from, could start combining and building the simplest atoms. Since it's only made of one proton and one electron, they don't get much simpler, or more common, than **HYDROGEN**, meaning there was lots and lots of hydrogen **floating** around in that early Universe. **GREAT BIG CLOUDS** of it.

1. Take one proton.

BUILD YOUR OWN HYDROGEN!

2. Take one electron.

What's on your shoe?

A clump!

3. Done!

(I'm going to talk about how all the big things get made in a moment and it means I'm going to use one of my favourite words in all space-talk; and that is ...

"**CLUMPING**". You don't get to say "**CLUMPING**" very often in the rest of life, but it's a great word. Bits of things just coming together in an uneven lump. It's what the dust did on your fingertip when you ran it across that high shelf a moment ago. Or when you've been playing with **PLAY-DOH** and there are bits of it everywhere and to tidy it up you get a big bit of Play-Doh and roll it over all the little bits, so they **stick together** into one **HUGE LUMP**: that's top-quality clumping right there.)

CLUMP

#1

LUMP

SQUISHY STARS

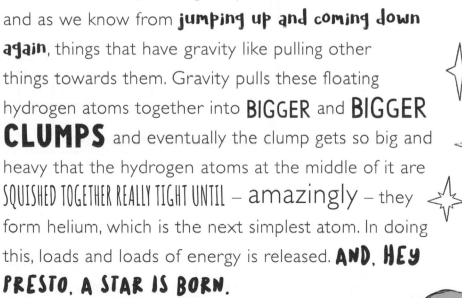

So we have loads of **hydrogen atoms** floating around, and while that feels like it would be really light, it still weighs something, and therefore it has specific gravity, and as we know from **jumping up and coming down again**, things that have gravity like pulling other things towards them. Gravity pulls these floating hydrogen atoms together into **BIGGER** and **BIGGER CLUMPS** and eventually the clump gets so big and heavy that the hydrogen atoms at the middle of it are SQUISHED TOGETHER REALLY TIGHT UNTIL – amazingly – they form helium, which is the next simplest atom. In doing this, loads and loads of energy is released. **AND, HEY PRESTO, A STAR IS BORN.**

You know when you get a piece of bread and SQUISH it in your hands, harder and harder, it eventually turns into **CHOCOLATE**? Yeah, just like that. What, has that never worked for you? Oh, you're just NOT SQUISHING hard enough. Try it again the next time you're having a meal with loads of other people. They'll be **EXCITED** to watch you.

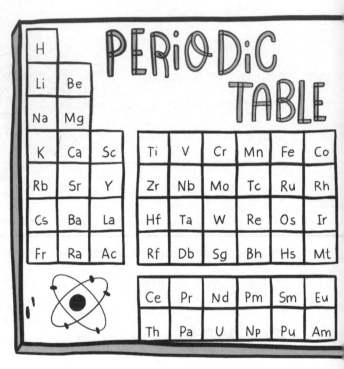

Anyway, the stars "burn" all their hydrogen (squishing it down and turning it into helium) and when they have run out of hydrogen, they start to SQUISH the helium together instead, into even more complicated elements, like **CARBON** or **OXYGEN**. Sometimes at the end of this whole process, depending on the size of the stars, there will be a **HUGE EXPLOSION**, called a **SUPERNOVA**, in which even heavier, more complicated elements are made, all the way up through the **periodic table**, our list of elements. This is how we get all our elements, by the way, which I've said before but is always worth repeating. **EVERY ATOM IN YOUR BODY WAS MADE IN THE HEART OF A STAR.** You may take a moment and enjoy how amazing that is.

									He
			B	C	N	O	F	Ne	
			Al	Si	P	S	Cl	Ar	
Ni	Cu	Zn	Ga	Ge	As	Se	Br	Kr	
Pd	Ag	Cd	In	Sn	Sb	Te	I	Xe	
Pt	Au	Hg	Tl	Pb	Bi	Po	At	Rn	
Ds	Rg	Cn	Nh	Fl	Mc	Lv	Ts	Og	

Gd	Tb	Dy	Ho	Er	Tm	Yb	Lu
Cm	Bk	Cf	Es	Fm	Md	No	Lr

OK, BACK TO DUST!

Did you clean your finger after you rubbed it along that shelf? Maybe do it now. I'll wait.

Finger clean? Lovely.

This process keeps happening – stars being made and then exploding and sending out heavier elements. **Throughout space there are huge clouds of dust.** If you want to see one of these clouds, look up at **Orion** at night, the coolest of all the constellations. **(There is a long explanation of why Orion is so cool in my other book about space: *Beyond the Sky*).** You'll see his "belt", which is made of three stars across his middle, and hanging down from the middle of the "belt" is his "sword", which also appears to be made of three stars, except that the middle of them looks a little "*FUZZIER*". Point a telescope at the fuzzy patch and you'll see it's not a star at all, but **a huge cloud of gas**

and dust called the ORION NEBULA, and one of the closest star-forming regions to Earth, a mere 1,344 light years away, which is just a little past twelve-and-a-half thousand, million, million kilometres away, which is why it looks a little faint and fuzzy.

The mass of that whole cloud is more than 2,000 times that of the Sun though, and it is thought that 700 different stars are being created there right now.

OUR SOLAR SYSTEM:
AN ORIGIN STORY

Before our Solar System was **born, there was a cloud,** one of many, floating quietly in space. Occasionally these clouds would get shaken, say by the aftershock of a nearby **supernova,** and the dust and gas would be thrown into a new **CLUMP** and the whole star-making process would begin.

This is what happened to create our **SOLAR SYSTEM** four-and-a-half billion years ago. **The Sun was created from a cloud of dust and gas,** and as it grew and its gravitational pull grew, it pulled in more than ninety-nine per cent of the matter available in the cloud.

That last one per cent might not sound like much, but it ends up being **very important** to our story.

The dust and gas left over from the cloud wasn't dragged into the new star. Instead, the gravity of the newly created, SPINNING STAR flattened the remaining dust outside it down into a disk, and then made the disk **spin**. It is from this dusty spinning disk that all the planets were made. They got made, as we're beginning to see, the way everything seems to get made, by **CLUMPING**.

In the spinning disk of dust, lumps began to form and they gathered up more dust as they spun, like your finger pulling more dust together as you ran it along the dusty shelf. They gathered into bigger and bigger lumps, gathering more and more dust until they were the biggest things in their parts of the disk. **And that's how the planets were created.**

Let's press fast-forward on all this clumping and see what our Solar System ended up looking like, four-and-a-half billion years later. Right in the middle is our Sun, burning away. **AS WE MOVE OUT FROM THE SUN WE FIND FOUR SMALL ROCKY PLANETS: MERCURY, VENUS, EARTH AND MARS.**

Outside of them is the **ASTEROID BELT**, which is more rocks, but smaller. (It's basically bits of rocks that didn't quite make it into being a planet. They weren't great at clumping.)

Moving further out we begin to meet **THE GAS GIANTS: JUPITER, SATURN, URANUS AND NEPTUNE**, all of them bigger

> No one would clump with me

than the four rocky planets, but mainly made of much lighter elements than the four planets further in. In fact, Saturn, even though it is huge, is so lacking in density that you could float it in a bath, if you had a bath big enough.

(Lots of people teach systems for how to remember the planets in order, usually by memorizing long sentences starting with the same letters, but I find those sentences more difficult to remember than the planets. **If you just remember that the Solar System starts with the Sun and ends with "S, U, N", which is Saturn, Uranus and Neptune, it's usually easy to fill in the blanks.**)

Outside those gas giants is the **Kuiper belt**, which, like the **asteroid belt**, is made of rocks and fragments of planets that didn't come together. Poor old Pluto is out here, flying around not being big and dominant enough to be a planet. ***POOR OLD PLUTO.*** Used to be a planet once. **Isn't a planet any more.** We don't talk about it in front of Pluto, but we know he keeps sending letters to the International Astronomical Federation under fake names asking if Pluto can be a planet again.

FROM: CONCERNED HUMAN

FROM: ASTER O:DBELT

FROM: Dr P. LUTO

TO:
ASTRONOMICAL INTERNATIONAL FEDERATION
EARTH STREET
PLANET EARTH
THE MILKY WAY

Outside that again is the **Oort cloud**, which is a huge sphere, all around our Solar System, of rocks and dust and comets and asteroids. Occasionally you hear of comets that only pass us at huge intervals, like **Halley's Comet**, which we see once every seventy-six years. These are Oort cloud objects, cutting huge orbits across the Solar System, dragged out of their lonely, distant orbits by the pull of the planets and sent touring round the Solar System instead.

So, our planetary system is **ROCK, ROCK, ROCK, ROCK** and then GAS, GAS, GAS, GAS.

This is because the Sun, being the big, massive, bossy thing that dictated everything, either pulled all the lighter elements near it into itself or **pushed** them further out with its radiation. It left lots of **HEAVIER DUST** that gathered, again by CLUMPING TOGETHER in the disk of dust, into those small, heavy, inner planets we have today, including our own.

SPHERES OF PROTECTION

This huge long process gave us our rocky planet, with a thin gassy atmosphere and a **HEAVY METAL CORE**, and all of that was vital to making life survive on Earth.

The Universe, and this is a point I will make many, many times in this book, is a stupidly difficult place to live. I mean, yes, it's the only place to live, since it's the Universe, so we have nowhere else to go, but still, it is **SO** unfriendly to life. We only survive on Earth because we live in the middle of a series of invisible spheres that protect us.

The hugest of these is the **Heliosphere**, which is a massive (way bigger than the Solar System) **magnetic field** caused by the Sun. This is **REALLY** important, because of a thing called "**cosmic radiation**", which is a really terrible, unhelpful thing. Basically, there are **FRAGMENTS** of atoms constantly ⊆ⁱⁿ∈∈₱ᵢₙ₉ through the Universe, moving at nearly the **speed of light**, that would wipe out any form of life they met. **This is cosmic radiation**. It is horrible stuff.

If it passes through the human body, it can break apart the cells and cause serious illnesses, like cancer. It's the reason people are very careful around nuclear power plants, and why, if you've ever had an **X-RAY** at the doctor's or dentist's, the person doing the X-ray stands away from the machine. **You have to limit your exposure to radiation.**

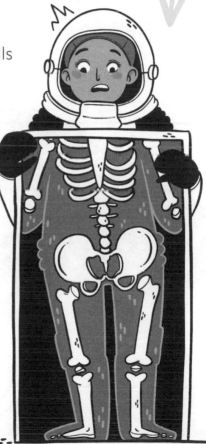

And cosmic radiation is a particularly energetic and damaging type of radiation. Even the SHORTEST exposure would be very damaging to our health.

SO - LUCKILY! - WE HAVE THE SUN AND ITS MAGNETIC FIELD. The Heliosphere deflects the cosmic radiation and keeps it from killing all life in the Solar System, including us.

It's like, it's constantly raining in space, but the Sun holds up a big umbrella and keeps us dry. Except, of course that it doesn't rain in space, so forget I ever said that.

The Heliosphere is also like the boundary of the Solar System, as, when you pass through it, you move from where the Sun is the most important thing, and the Universe takes over. **WE ARE SAFELY INSIDE THE HELIOSPHERE.**

That is the first sphere. However, the Sun also spits out radiation, at least some of which you'll be familiar with, because of **SUNTANS**. There is a lot more to the Sun's radiation than that though, **so we're lucky we have our second sphere**.

Because we have iron in our planet's core, we also have our own magnetic field right here, which you already know because, y'know, compasses work. **Earth's magnetic field** gives us even more deflecting power to **BOUNCE** the radiation away. You can see that in action if you have ever seen the **Northern Lights**, also known as the **Aurora Borealis** – huge, gorgeous, swoops of green and blue in the sky, where radiation from the Sun meets the Earth's magnetic field, charging it with energy, until it snaps back and releases the energy in **a spectacular light show in the sky**. We call them the Northern Lights here, because we're used to thinking of them as something that happens the further north you go; but, of course, there are Southern Lights as

well, the Aurora Australis, which you can see as you approach the South Pole.

VENUS AND MARS (AND THE MOON)

don't have a metal core, so they don't have their own magnetic field. That makes them very dangerous places to visit without proper protection against radiation. Any mission to those planets (or even to the Moon, which passes outside our magnetic field) has to take into account the effect of the radiation, and the dangers of long-term damage to human health.

A BIT OF ATMOSPHERE

Then there is the most important sphere of all, the atmosphere, that thin blanket of GASES around the planet. The atmosphere can extend as far as 300 kilometres up from Earth, but by then, the air is

INCREDIBLY THIN. The more commonly used boundary is at 100 kilometres up, which is where outer space legally begins. **You're not an astronaut until you hit 100 kilometres up.**

And while 100 kilometres sounds like a lot, the radius of the entire planet is about 6,300 kilometres, so our atmosphere is only one-and-a-half per cent of the total. It really is the MOST NARROW, DELICATE AND VITAL THING. Take a football and wet it. We're basically saying that all life, all the life we've ever known, exists in that thin layer of fluid on the surface.

We take that blanket of gases for granted because we **swim** through it every day, but not every planet has that **perfect mix** between land and air.

MERCURY

MERCURY, the nearest planet to the Sun, has **no atmosphere** at all and very little fun either. It's so close to the Sun that all the `lighter elements got blown away` by the star's energy. Mercury has the shortest "year" of any planet in the Solar System, **taking only eighty-eight days to go around the Sun**. However, the "day" on Mercury (the amount of time it takes to spin around itself) is really long, about fifty-nine Earth days. So as it travels around the Sun, it slowly spins, like those chickens on the rotating shelves in the supermarket.

The side of Mercury facing the Sun gets heated to 450 degrees Celsius, over four times the boiling temperature of water. Meanwhile, since there is no atmosphere to hold the temperature, the other side cools down as it faces the darkness of space, way beyond the freezing temperature of water, and reaches -170 degrees Celsius. **And slowly it spins from hot to cold.**

PING!

00:00

MERCURY iS DONE

If Mercury had an atmosphere, **enormous winds** would carry the heat from one side of planet to the other. That would even the temperature a bit, but it would mean that if there was life on Mercury, it would have to put up with **CONSTANT WINDS BLOWING AT HUNDREDS OF KILOMETRES AN HOUR**. Mercurians would communicate by shouting, a lot. But Mercury has no atmosphere, and in those extreme conditions, no life.

Venus has an atmosphere, but as I have said many times before, **DON'T GO TO VENUS**. IT IS HORRIBLE. It's even hotter than Mercury because the atmosphere keeps all the heat in, plus winds can reach over 3,750 km/h (which is 100 metres a second!) and **the atmosphere is made of burning acids**. Even when we have managed to land unmanned spacecrafts on Venus, their missions have been hilariously short-lived.

The Russians have sent a series of missions to Venus:

- **Venera 3** crash-landed on to the surface in 1966, which sounds like a failure, but it nevertheless became the first human-made craft to reach another planet.

- **Venera 4's** battery ran out on its descent.

- **Venera 5 and 6** were both crushed by the huge atmospheric pressure.

- **Venera 7** landed on the surface! It sent back the exciting news that the surface temperature was 455 to 475 degrees Celsius, and after twenty-three minutes it stopped working, mainly due to the temperature being between 455 and 475 degrees Celsius.

- In 1978, NASA sent the **Venus Multiprobe**, consisting of four separate probes. Only one made it to the surface and it survived for forty-five minutes.

- **Venera 12** survived for 110 minutes! Nearly two hours! The length of a movie! THEN VENUS KILLED IT AS WELL.

And that is the best we've done.

Venus is horrible.

EARTH'S AMAZING ATMOSPHERE

Let's look at our lovely Earth atmosphere instead. Go on, breathe it in. Lovely, isn't it? Lovely and vital. The **ATMOSPHERE IS VITAL TO LIFE ON EARTH** for a load of reasons other than it being something good to breathe.

For a start – and this is the **SINGLE MOST IMPORTANT THING** – if we didn't have an atmosphere, we couldn't fly paper planes. Seriously, try it. **Go into a room and suck all the air out.** Take a load of deep breaths and then blow the air out of the keyhole in the door or up the chimney, until there is only one lungful of air left in the room. Then very quickly inhale that last lungful, make a paper plane, throw it and watch it drop to the ground immediately *(just before you pass out)*.

Actually, don't do any of that. It is all silly and impossible and if somebody grown up was reading it out to you and **DIDN'T** stop midway through with a confused look on their face, then give them a stern look and never trust them again. **Paper planes fly because they glide across the molecules of air.** Without that sea of air, they simply couldn't fly. (And neither could their bigger, **heavier, metal cousins: ACTUAL AEROPLANES**. Or for that matter, **BIRDS**.)

Similarly, without an atmosphere we would have no wind, so no kites, no windmills, and flags would just hang limply. However, I suspect you are looking for a better reason to applaud the atmosphere.

Well, there's the **TEMPERATURE**, I suppose. This thin duvet of gas we sleep under is perfectly designed to keep the Earth at a liveable temperature. **Sunlight is caught by the molecules of air** and spread about the planet by the weather, and even when some of the planet is out of direct light, the atmosphere holds the reflected energy from the surface, preventing the night-time side from becoming too cold. **REMEMBER HOW MERCURY WENT FROM SEARINGLY HOT TO FREEZING COLD AS THE PLANET SPUN?** None of that for us.

We packed the wrong clothes for Mercury

And although you might feel the change in temperature a bit if you've ever flown home from your holidays still in your shorts, and arrived in a cold wintry airport at home, it's not "dropping 300 degrees" bad.

The **Moon** also has no atmosphere, because its gravity is too small to hold on to it and, again, there the temperatures veer violently from 127 degrees Celsius in the sun, to -173 degrees Celsius in the shade.

THE MOON IS ALSO "TIDALLY LOCKED" TO US, which means that over time its rotation has fallen in step with its orbit. This is why we always see the same side of the Moon from Earth. **Look up at the Moon, memorize all the different patches and craters, and then look away and - quickly! - turn back when the Moon isn't expecting it! Look! Same stuff.** The Moon has never been caught out by this trick. It always keeps the same side hidden.

An atmosphere is also very good at moving water around the planet, in the form of

WEATHER, so that it can evaporate off the oceans, rain on to the mountains, flow back down to the sea, and generally be available for living things all over the globe. If we didn't have an atmosphere, water would simply evaporate from the surface of the planet, and only be found trapped beneath the surface, which would be no use if you were thirsty, or wanted to water the garden.

DO YOU WANT EVEN MORE REASONS WHY AN ATMOSPHERE IS BRILLIANT?

Earlier, we mentioned all that radiation in space, and the atmosphere is a last shield against that, absorbing or deflecting loads of dangerous particles and rays. More dramatically though, the atmosphere

burns up all sorts of debris before it can land on our heads. **NASA estimates that 100 tonnes of space debris strikes Earth every day**, mostly in the form of dust or tiny particles. When they hit the atmosphere, the friction of passing through the air makes them burn up, sometimes as beautiful "**shooting stars**".

NEXT TIME YOU MAKE A WISH ON A SHOOTING STAR, remember that is a piece of space dust, often dropped by comets, and then set aflame by the **upper atmosphere**. And make a wish that this protective work by our atmosphere continues, so that we don't end up like the **DINOSAURS**.

So there is all that, and we haven't even mentioned the **OXYGEN** we breathe, which makes up a fifth of the air around us. Oxygen is an element that combines easily and often very energetically with other **atoms** and **molecules** like, for example, in a fire. This means that it can be used to **STORE ENERGY** and then release it later, say, as part of a barbecue, or, more commonly, and usefully, in the cells of our body, burning the fuel we eat and keeping us warm and alive. **Oxygen is really, really useful for life.**

So, yes, fair point, there is more to the atmosphere than **PAPER PLANES**, but only just.

So, we started with a **cloud of dust and gas**, and four-and-a-half billion years later we have the Sun offering heat and protection, a metal core keeping the radiation away, an atmosphere regulating the temperature, liquid water and oxygen.

And then life came along.

Some years later, in Clara's laboratory...

WHAT IS LIFE ANYWAY?

YEAH, WHAT IS LIFE?

This seems like an easy question to answer. Animals, right? Big furry ones and wet slippery ones and ones that fly. That covers it. Oh, and insects as well. We almost forgot insects. **So life is anything that runs around, or flies or swims and eats things and gets eaten by other things.**

(COUGHING NOISE) AHEM, said the houseplant sitting on the desk. What about us?

So, yes, of course, we have to include **plants** and **trees** and **grasses** and **ferns** and all that stuff. They don't move anywhere or eat anything (other than Venus flytraps and we definitely have to have a proper talk about them some time; they must be aliens), but they grow, and they create new life. These are all pretty big, though. **WHAT ABOUT ALL THE LITTLE THINGS?** The bugs , the germs, the bacteria, and even the organisms we have recently discovered in the most inhospitable places, **THE EXTREMOPHILES**, that can live by the volcanic jets deep down under the sea or **FROZEN** in the Arctic snow.

Don't forget me!

The problem is that though it's easy to say, "**That's alive!**" when you're petting your dog, or picking an apple off a tree, in a more general way, IT'S VERY DIFFICULT TO NARROW DOWN A GOOD DEFINITION OF LIFE.

Traditionally we would say something like (COUGH, CLEARS THROAT), "Life is the ability to reproduce and spread!" but then, **by that definition, FIRE IS ALIVE.**

I'm alive!

So let's make it more complicated and say (COUGH, CLEARS THROAT AGAIN), "Life is the ability to take energy or matter from the environment and use it to help reproduce!" This sounds pretty good, but if you've ever made a crystal from one of those kits where you dip a string in a glass for a couple of weeks, it definitely uses matter from its environment to make more crystals. **And you would never say a CRYSTAL WAS ALIVE.**

But whatever definition we settle on for "life", it'll have to include everything from animals we can interact with (dogs, people, a moose) all the way down to things we can only see under a microscope (bacteria, viruses and the like).

The chances are though, and this is sort of disappointing, that in our search for life on other planets we're **far more** likely to discover things from the TINY END of that list rather than the **LARGE, FURRY END.** Because the small stuff has just been around for **so much longer**.

If you look at the history of life on Earth, the **BIG, COMPLEX, FURRY, TALKING CREATURES** arrived pretty late in the process. And it was a very long process. **It was more like a Sunday roast than a microwave dinner**, if the Sunday roast took four billion years, including having to wait 3.999 billion years for the chickens to evolve.

Even if we found an **exact replica of Earth** somewhere out there tomorrow, orbiting around an **exact double of our Sun**,

at exactly the same distance, it could be at **any stage of this life-cooking process**. But the chances of you arriving just as the people of Earth 2 are evolved enough to recognize what you are and have a chat with you about your day are pretty slim.

HI, ALIEN GUY, WE SAVED YOU A SEAT!

HOW DOES LIFE BEGIN?

WE DON'T EVEN FULLY KNOW HOW LIFE BEGAN ON EARTH, but there are a number of theories that share the same basic idea – **THERE WAS A MIX OF CHEMICALS AND AN ENERGY SOURCE** – and somehow that mix of chemicals, as they reacted with each other, hit on a configuration that could **build copies of itself**.

Obviously, we're going a long way back here, so the exact details are still a little vague.

We know the Earth is about **4.5 billion years old**.

We think there were oceans on Earth from about **4.4 billion years ago**.

We also think life began somewhere between **4.2 and 3.8 billion years ago**, but it definitely happened at about 4.25pm on a Friday afternoon just in time for the weekend, **so that all the new animals had a little time to relax before starting work on Monday**.

ONE POPULAR THEORY is that life began deep in the oceans, around underwater thermal vents, where the right kind of chemicals, rich in hydrogen, were thrown up into the sea by the vents. The chemicals mixed in the warm water near the volcanic jets until they began to make the useful chemical compounds that became **THE BUILDING BLOCKS FOR LIFE**.

ANOTHER POPULAR THEORY is that the necessary mix of hydrogen, nitrogen and carbon were already in those early oceans and that **lightning strikes** from the turbulent early Earth weather provided the sudden **BURST** of energy that made the **chemicals bond**.

In a famous experiment in 1953, the chemists **Harold Urey** and **Stanley Miller** tried to recreate the conditions at the start of life, but in a laboratory. They mixed the chemicals most likely to have been in the early ocean and then repeatedly **UNLEASHED ELECTRICAL BURSTS**, to mimic lightning. **Then they waited until something crawled out of the jar and asked them to stop.**

No, wait, that would have been silly.

They left the experiment running and after a couple of weeks the clear water had turned brown. When they tested the resulting **GLOOP**, they found it contained **five different amino acids**, which aren't living things themselves, but are vital building blocks of life. To make it even more realistic, they later repeated the experiment, but this time they added to the mix a gas called hydrogen sulphide, a gas commonly released by **volcanoes**. (Earth, in the early days, had a **LOT** of volcanoes.)

This time the number of amino acids rose to twenty-seven, hinting further that **early Earth, despite being clearly a scary place covered in volcanoes and lightning, was a pretty good baking tray for life**.

INCREDIBLE EVOLUTION

The journey from those simple chemicals, all the way to you holding this book, though, is a very, **very long one**. For the first couple of **BILLION YEARS** it was just the tiny things: **bacteria, viruses and single-celled creatures**. A visit to Earth at this time would not have been entertaining. But that doesn't mean great things weren't happening.

For example, about **THREE BILLION YEARS AGO**, some of those little things learned how to do **PHOTOSYNTHESIS**, which would turn out to be a very useful skill, like learning how to do long division, or riding a

Nothing to see here

What a waste of petrol

bicycle or making a great boiled egg (four-and-a-half minutes for really good dunkiness, but always put the egg in warm water when you take it out of the fridge, or the shell will crack in the boiling water).

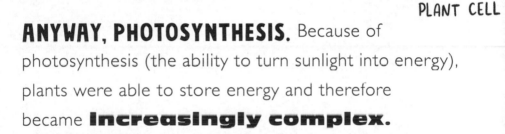

CARBON DIOXIDE

SUNLIGHT

OXYGEN

HUNGRY PLANT CELL

ANYWAY, PHOTOSYNTHESIS. Because of photosynthesis (the ability to turn sunlight into energy), plants were able to store energy and therefore became **increasingly complex.**

That said, it was only about a billion years ago that we began to see the first **multicellular life**. **This was a huge step in evolution, and it took three billion years!** Life was still only something you could see through a microscope. **YIKES, THIS IS SLOW.**

One hundred million years later, the first **SPONGES** appeared. Immediately all the surfaces got a lot cleaner, which was a relief because, honestly, **early Earth was a real mess.**

As the years tick by we start to see **more** and **more complex creatures**: jellyfish, worms, anemones and corals, until we reach an important date: 540 million years ago and what we call the **CAMBRIAN EXPLOSION**, although not for the fun fireworks-type reason you might think.

When we look at evidence of this era, we see a massive increase in the number of **FOSSILS**, either because there was a massive increase in the number of animals, or just a massive increase in animals falling dead into sand and becoming fossils. Either way, the cast list of life **expands** enormously, and we begin to meet genuinely complex animals. **Trilobites** appear here, as do the first animals with proper **backbones**, and immediately there is a huge increase in the number of parents of animals-with-backbones, telling them not to slouch.

Life isn't just in the sea any more either.
Plants and animals have started exploring the land. Insects appeared 400 million years ago, and 397 million years ago, the first four-legged creature crawled out of the sea helpfully leaving a fossilised **FOOTPRINT**. Any point from here on would be a great time to visit the planet. Loads of animals to see (and to avoid being eaten by) and occasionally a **COMET CRASHES IN AND PRESSES THE RESET BUTTON.**

Dinosaurs, tortoises, crocodiles and sharks all appear and some of them disappear. Well, the dinosaurs disappear, **which is a pity since they were OBVIOUSLY AMAZING**, and, in many ways, nothing has been as great since. The largest ever land mammal, for example, the SAUROPOD, had its moment about 100 million years ago. Farewell, sauropod, you remain undefeated. You still cast a huge shadow.

Farewell to the dinosaurs, then, and all the other animals that didn't make it through ICE AGES and **comet strikes** and other great extinction events. Despite these challenges, life clings on, keeps regrouping and diversifying.

THE GREAT FAMILIES OF ANIMALS EXPAND: FISH, BIRDS, REPTILES, AMPHIBIANS AND MAMMALS. And within mammals, our family, the primates, almost the last to appear, arrive about eighty-five million years ago. Within that family, there come the apes, and then, about six million years ago, humans arrive, in rough form, and only recently separated from our nearest cousins, the chimps.

Another couple of million years of standing up straighter and straighter until eventually, only 50,000 years ago,
WE APPEAR!

Four billion years of life, starting from the basic building blocks, and ending up with you holding this book.

And after that, we took the rest of the weekend off. Phew.

IS THERE LIFE
BEYOND EARTH?

THAT'S HOW IT ALL HAPPENED ON

EARTH, anyway, although we skipped a lot to save on time. But the other planets in our **Solar System** have had just as long, and in that four billion years we've made giraffes and poisonous frogs and parrots that can say "**HELLO**", so just imagine what **mad-headed things** we're going to find on the other planets in our Solar System!

Hey, I forgot to ask this earlier! What sort of aliens do you want to meet?

Ones we could have a conversation with would be good, although there may be **MANY, MANY REASONS WHY THAT WILL BE DIFFICULT** (which we will cover later). But that would be the main dream, obviously: to meet an alien race we could compare spacecraft

with, and learn new technologies
from, and maybe have a few adventures with,
where it all goes **PEW-PEW-PEW** with the
LASER GUNS and eventually overthrowing
AN EVIL GALACTIC EMPIRE at the end.

But basically something we could be friends with...

Well, let's get the bad news out of the way.

Our Solar System is pretty **unfriendly** towards
life – certainly to the kind of life it would be fun to
hang out with.

Take a look at our nearest neighbours, the inner planets.

Mercury is cold **AND** hot, and has no atmosphere, and it lives right next door to the Sun and so anything trying to live there would be **ZAPPED** pretty immediately.

Venus has an atmosphere, but is ridiculously, metal-meltingly hot, and the sky is filled with huge clouds of **sulphuric acid**. If there is life, it might only be **tiny bacteria** living high in the atmosphere, and where's the fun in that? Nobody wants to hang out with a bacterium, or take it for a walk, or go on space adventures with it. **(Besides, you probably have at least ten different types of bacteria up your nose right now, so bring them for a walk instead.)**

Mars has only a THIN atmosphere – it has no rocky core, so most of its atmosphere was blown away long

ago by **RADIATION** from the Sun. There is very little oxygen, but loads and loads of carbon dioxide, which we can't breathe. Mars used to have water, perhaps **huge** oceans of it, but now water can only exist as either solid ice, underground, or vapour in the air. And life is difficult to sustain with only ice and water vapour.

SO, OUR NEARBY PLANETS ARE A MESS.

Too hot, or too cold, or both at the same time. Too much air pressure, or too little, or no atmosphere at all. Too close to the Sun or too far away.

AND HERE WE ARE, IN THE MIDDLE OF THEM,

with just the right mix of all these things. Just the right amount of atmosphere and just the right gases in it. Just the right distance from the Sun, so that we can have just the right amount of heat, so that water can flow as a liquid.

It seems that there is a thin disk around the Sun, called the "HABITABLE ZONE": a region of space that gets just the right amount of energy to make life liveable. **And Earth sits just in it.**

Scientists have a special name for describing something that's **not too hot** and **not too cold**.

IT'S LIKE THAT FAIRY TALE OF THE THREE BEARS, who made porridge in the morning but Daddy's porridge was **TOO HOT**, so he insisted they all go for a really long walk in the woods, even though Baby Bear's porridge was the **PERFECT TEMPERATURE** and Mummy Bear's was just **A LITTLE COLD**, and she could have just popped it in the microwave for a minute, while Daddy blew on his porridge and was just a tiny bit patient with it. But no, Daddy Bear had to demand they all immediately go for a walk, and in such a rush that they didn't even have time to lock the door and any passing child could just walk in and **SMASH UP**

the furniture, and mess up the beds, and fall asleep exhausted. And this is why scientists call the perfect distance from the Sun, for the existence of life, the "Daddy Bear should have just blown on his porridge" Zone.

No, wait, that's wrong.

They call it the **GOLDILOCKS ZONE**.

Not too hot, not too cold. Just right for life. And that's where Earth is. And none of the other planets are in that zone.

Too hot

Just right

Too cold

IF WE GO OUT EVEN FURTHER, TO THE GAS GIANTS, THE STORY DOESN'T GET MUCH BETTER.

Jupiter is mainly made of hydrogen and helium but has thick clouds of ammonia and sulphur, which are corrosive and poisonous, and that's before you take into account the 500 km/h winds. Plus, we're not even sure if there is a core there or if it is just **FLUIDS** all the way to the middle, although by that stage they would be SQUEEZED BY THE INCREDIBLE PRESSURE into some weird, dense soup. And I know you've

probably eaten some weird, dense soups in your life, but this is properly yucky. **Basically, we're not expecting a call from the people of Jupiter any time soon.**

Saturn isn't much better. More hydrogen and helium, and **no real core to land on, or live on**. It's also getting pretty cold at that distance from the Sun. Average temperatures on Saturn can be around **-174 degrees Celsius**.

It gets even colder on the two more distant planets, the **ICE GIANTS** of Uranus and Neptune, where it can reach as low as **-214 degrees Celsius**. Uranus would be particularly weird to live on, especially at the poles, since the entire planet's rotation is tilted so much that each pole spends TWENTY-ONE YEARS in unbroken winter night-time, and then, later, **twenty-one years in uninterrupted summer day-time.**

Not that there is a great deal of warmth in a day-time nearly **three billion kilometres** from the Sun, *TWENTY TIMES FURTHER OUT THAN EARTH*.

In general it seems that massive atmospheric pressure, poisonous gases, no actual surfaces and freezing temperatures would make it **UNBELIEVABLY DIFFICULT FOR LIFE TO SURVIVE**, let alone evolve, on our neighbouring planets.

IF IT WORKS HERE...

So should we write off the Solar System?

MAYBE NOT JUST YET.

Let's have a look again at life on Earth and see what lessons there might be for where life could exist. After all, until we actually meet an alien, we have to speculate about what they might be like. But when I say speculate, **DON'T GO TOTALLY MAD...**

Aliens will be like a gorilla, but blue, and with metal legs!

Just a giant bouncing foot!

A cloud of gas, wearing a dickie bow!

Our speculation has to be a mixture of Pure Imagination and Science. By which I mean, we should

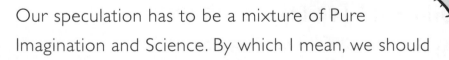

be all **serious and sciencey** and put on a lab coat and frown in a thoughtful way and do the sensible thing: look at the **huge** variety of animals walking, flying, farting and sleeping all over our lovely planet and make a good estimation that "if it works here, it'll work out there in space as well". And **THEN** we can use Pure Imagination to make them all blue and give them metal legs.

FOR EXAMPLE, we have plenty of animals who fly. Birds, obviously, and bees and butterflies and Mary Poppins and those **GLIDING SQUIRRELS** whose arms look like wings, although what they are really doing is **controlled falling**. The one thing they all have in common though is that they all use the **GASES IN THE ATMOSPHERE TO PUSH AGAINST**.

If you put an eagle in the near-
total vacuum of space, it would
have no air to flap against and it
wouldn't be able to fly at all. Plus, it
wouldn't be able to breathe, and the cold would be
very bad for it, so basically **PUTTING AN EAGLE
IN SPACE IS A TERRIBLE IDEA**. Ironically, the
first Moon-lander was called *Eagle*, despite it being a
TERRIBLE CHOICE OF ANIMAL. Although
they were probably more interested in what the eagle
represented.

Anyway, if an alien planet has an `atmosphere`, even with gases different to ours, **there might be an animal there that can fly**. That would be an interesting, justifiable guess to make.

As we've already mentioned, yes, some of our Solar System planets have atmospheres, but they are made of **HORRIBLE POISONOUS GASES** a lot of the time, so we don't think life has much of a chance of getting a foothold on even the smallest level, a long way before we get anything as amazing as birds. Or Mary Poppins.

A **better hint** might be that we have **plenty of animals on Earth** who swim. Tropical fish swim in hot water. Over 240 types of Arctic fish swim in very cold water, wondering why they aren't tropical fish. Even down in the very depths of the ocean where no sunlight can penetrate, there are over **200 different kinds of anglerfish,** the ugly fish that carries its own **light bulb** around to attract other fish it can eat.

ANGLERFISH ARE AMAZING. They live so deep in the ocean, we didn't even know they existed until one washed up on the shores of Greenland in 1833. Even then we couldn't study them properly until we were able to spend time at their depths. **THAT LIGHT THEY CARRY IS MADE FROM LUMINOUS BACTERIA**, and while many of them have their light at the end of a growth from their head (shaped like a fishing rod, hence the name), there is one species that has the lightbulb at the back of their mouth. If you see that, it is already too late, little fish.

The largest kind of **anglerfish** are called **warty seadevils** (which is how you insult a fisherman – try it next time you meet a fisherman), and while the female warty seadevils can grow up to two-and-a-half feet (76cm) long, the males  are, amazingly, less than an inch (2.5cm) long, and just attach to the female's belly and swim alongside for life.

To these fish, add all the other swimmers of the world – whales, dolphins, eels and turtles – not to mention that we think life itself may have started in depths around **underwater volcanic vents**. It's probably a good guess that a planet with water, or indeed any stable liquid, might have swimming animals in it as well. **And while none of the other planets in our Solar System have liquid water, the story is far more hopeful if we widen our search to look at their moons...**

LIFE ON THE MOONS?

We always call the Moon, THE Moon. We should really call it **OUR** Moon, because there are loads of other moons in the Solar System, maybe as many as **214**, orbiting the planets. **MARS HAS TWO FOR A START, PHOBOS AND DEIMOS**, although they are pretty tiny. Deimos's gravitational pull is one-thousandth that of Earth and, as I never get tired of telling people, **if you could run fast enough on it, you could jump right off**. Which would be amazing except that you'd have nowhere to go then except to crash-land on Mars.

The further we go, the more interesting the moons get and, most excitingly for us, some are thought to have oceans of water. **ORBITING AROUND JUPITER IS EUROPA**, a moon similar in size to our own. All we can see of it is its icy shell, believed to be up to thirty kilometres thick, but we know that **underneath there are oceans larger than all those on Earth combined.** In 2024, Nasa is sending out a special spaceship, the *Europa Clipper*, just to explore this moon. Similarly, **GANYMEDE AND CALLISTO, ALSO ORBITING JUPITER**, are believed to have sub-surface oceans, but possibly under as much as **150 TO 250 KILOMETRES OF ICE.** So not great places to search for, or indeed hope for, life.

An even better candidate might be **ENCELADUS, A MOON OF SATURN**, which also has this crunchy shell/yummy ocean-filling shape, but with the **added excitement of huge, gassy plumes of water bursting through cracks in the surface, like geysers.** This is not only a great sign that there is energy contained there, which is necessary for life, but also means that we could fly through the plumes and see what chemicals are being expelled. The *Cassini* probe flew to **Saturn in 2005** and spent more than **A DECADE EXPLORING THE PLANET AND ITS MOONS**. It was

I SMELL LIFE! IT SMELLS... OF CHEESE

Cassini that discovered these huge plumes bursting from Enceladus in the first place (they are far too faint to be seen from Earth) and in 2015, on one of its last missions, *Cassini* flew down to the surface of Enceladus, within three kilometres of the ice, and tried to pick up the scent of life.

It's important to say that this was not the job *Cassini* was built for, but it still managed to measure that the plumes were about **one per cent hydrogen** and about **0.5 per cent carbon dioxide**, both of **which are gases commonly associated with life**, particularly around volcanic vents, like the ones we find at the bottom of the oceans on Earth.

Staying near Saturn, we find another great candidate for life on the moon **TITAN**. Unlike the icy-shell moons we've already mentioned here, Titan has got actual **SURFACE LIQUID**, although maybe not the most hospitable kind. Titan has a sea called the **KRAKEN MAR** at one of its poles, and it is about the same size as the Caspian Sea (our largest inland sea) on Earth. However, it isn't water in Titan's sea, salty or otherwise. **THE KRAKEN MAR IS PREDOMINANTLY MADE OF METHANE**, a gas made up of carbon and hydrogen. On the one hand this is great, because carbon is the chemical which turns up in most of the chemicals of life. **On the other hand, methane is the gas that gives farts their distinctive smell**, so an entire ocean of that might not be the place to visit for a water-skiing holiday.

TITAN WATERSPORTS

FOR REN
Waterskis & Nose Pegs

These are all good candidates for finding life, and we can make some guesses as to what sort of creatures might survive in these worlds. On Europa and Enceladus, they would have to be creatures that could swim, and endure cold and darkness. On Titan they would have to have **NO NOSE**.

LIVING AT THE EXTREMES

These are pretty **severe** environments, and you've probably noticed that they seem to lie a long way outside the so-called "**Goldilocks Zone**" of distance from the Sun, where life is most likely to thrive. Of course, some parts of Earth are also pretty **INHOSPITABLE** to life and we've still managed to find microbes that live in boiling hot water, in burning acid and even in nuclear reactors. These are the "**EXTREMOPHILES**"; living creatures who thrive in the **worst environments**.

In **Chile's Atacama Desert**, one of the driest places on Earth, **Dunaliella algae** can survive by collecting the tiny amounts of dew that gather on spider's webs.

Bacteria, fungi and algae have been found in the frozen oceans of the Antarctic and in ice sheets in Siberia. The strongest of all (it's in the *Guinness Book of World Records*, although it probably doesn't know) is **Deinococcus radiodurans**, bacteria that can endure a burst of radiation 1,500 times **stronger** than one that would kill a human. This little toughie can also survive **FREEZING COLD**, **no water**, ACID and living in a vacuum. It seems the perfect candidate to pop up somewhere else in **SPACE**.

But, as I've often said here, it's hard to get TOO EXCITED about bacteria. Is there not a creature that might be this tough but still look like an animal? You know, something with some legs, and maybe a face?

LADIES AND GENTLEMEN, I GIVE YOU ... THE TARDIGRADE!

ALSO KNOWN AS THE WATER BEAR!

ALSO KNOWN AS THE MOSS PIGLET!

THEY EVEN FEATURED ON AN EPISODE OF OCTONAUTS ONCE!

TARDIGRADES ARE AMAZING. They have eight legs and a face and are totally an animal, although technically they are called a "micro-animal" because they can only be seen under a microscope. They grow to as much as half a millimetre in length though, so it doesn't even have to be that powerful a microscope, and that is WAAAAAAY BIGGER THAN BACTERIA.

AND THEY ARE TOUGH. They have been found on Himalayan mountains, in hot springs, in the deep oceans, at the South Pole and the equator, and under layers of ice. THEY CAN LIVE WITHOUT FOOD OR WATER FOR THIRTY YEARS, be frozen to -270 degrees Celsius and endure radiation 1,000 times stronger than other animals. BEST OF ALL, WE'VE SENT THEM INTO SPACE. NOT INSIDE A ROCKET EITHER. PROPERLY IN SPACE.

IN SEPTEMBER 2007, THE EUROPEAN SPACE AGENCY SENT TARDIGRADES UP ON A RUSSIAN LOW-EARTH ORBIT MISSION. For ten days, the tardigrades were exposed to the full vacuum of space. On their return, two-thirds of them were rehydrated and were back moving within half an hour. Like I said, tardigrades are **tough**.

KEEPING OUR BACTERIA TO OURSELVES

OF COURSE, THESE ARE ALL EARTH CREATURES. They are a good example of how life here can survive in **extreme conditions**, but they are also a **WARNING**. If these worlds we explore in space are pristine and devoid of life, then we might not want to walk some of our life on to them, on the soles of our shoes. We have no way of guaranteeing that a space probe sent from Earth doesn't have some **microscopic bacteria hiding** in its corners.

WE WANT TO DISCOVER LIFE ON OTHER PLANETS, NOT TAKE IT THERE.

And sometimes we have to take EXPLOSIVE precautions not to do that.

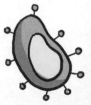

In 2004, **NASA's Cassini probe** arrived at Saturn after a seven-year journey from Earth. Over the next twelve years, it explored the rings, the **moons** and the planet itself, and made many of the discoveries I've mentioned already here. Cassini discovered the lakes of  **methane** on the giant moon Titan, the first liquid found on any body in the **Solar System** apart from Earth. Cassini discovered the jets of water shooting out of the surface of Enceladus and the huge seas of water under the **ICE SHELL** surface. Cassini sent us pictures of lightning on Saturn and discovered more moons and more rings than we could ever see from Earth. **BY ANY MEASURE, CASSINI HAD DONE A BRILLIANT JOB.**

However, by 2017, Cassini's fuel was beginning to run out, and it was at risk of ending the mission out of NASA's control, and with the possibility of crashing into one of the very moons it had revealed so much about.

The **huge danger** would be that, after giving us two really interesting candidates for moons where alien life might exist, Titan and Enceladus, Cassini might accidentally crash on to one of them and **contaminate** them with Earth life instead. So, a dramatic, SELF-DESTRUCTIVE conclusion to Cassini's mission was chosen instead. The probe's path was redirected so it travelled IN BETWEEN the rings and Saturn, **over and over again**, for a total of twenty-two orbits, edging closer and closer to the planet until, eventually, it came just too close to Saturn's atmosphere and it began to **BURN UP**, just like a **meteorite** would on Earth.

On 15 September 2017, Cassini burned through the upper atmosphere at 140,000 km/h, ending its mission as a **SHOOTING STAR** in the skies of Saturn.

There are times where we have been less heroic, and less successful, in our efforts to keep space clean of Earth life. **The Moon**, for example, our Moon, definitely had some Earth bacteria on it for a while, inside the **BAGS OF POO** left behind by the Apollo astronauts. Did you think they carried all their poo home with them? **No, they did not. In fact, the six missions that landed on the Moon left ninety-six bags behind**, filled with poo, wee, unfinished food and other rubbish. **And poo is fifty-five per cent bacteria**, so for a while at least, the Moon had life other than human life living on it.

And it's not the only time.

Do you remember the **TARDIGRADES** from earlier, the resilient micro-animals that we know could survive space? **I mean, we wouldn't want to crash a load of tardigrades into the Moon by accident, would we?**

What I'm saying is, you'd think we'd be careful not to slam a load of tough, almost impossible to kill, **space-surviving water bears** into the lunar surface ... by accident?

But, of course, that is exactly what we did. On 11 April 2019, the Israeli Beresheet mission, the first ever privately funded lunar lander, **CRASHED INTO**

THE MOON. Onboard was a special miniature library of thousands of books, left as a record of human civilization, and included within that were human DNA samples and … **THOUSANDS OF TARDIGRADES**.

This payload may have survived the violent impact, or maybe it got torn open and released the thousands of tardigrades to a new home to call their own. Maybe that is where we should wave: to the Moon. To the population of miniature water bears, sitting on the lunar surface with their new best friends, the poo bacteria, building a New World in space.

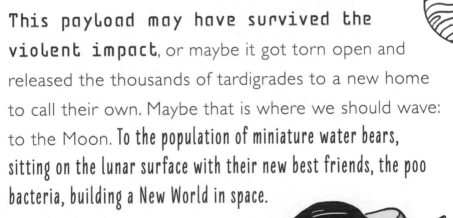

THIS IS ONE MICROSCOPIC STEP FOR A TARDIGRADE...

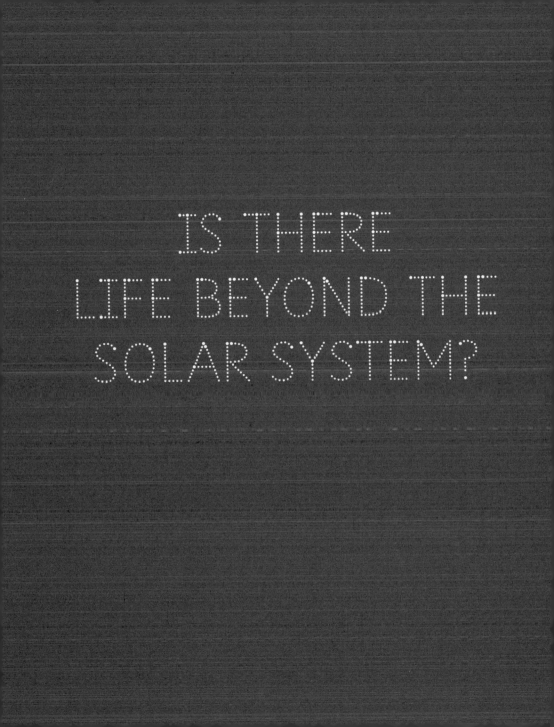

IS THERE
LIFE BEYOND THE
SOLAR SYSTEM?

So, there is almost **DEFINITELY NO LIFE** on the planets of the Solar System. Fine. There are loads of stars and loads of other planets.

We'll find other planets! That can't be difficult. Right?

Except, of course, it is fiendishly difficult and very rarely done.

DISCOVERING THE PLANETS

The first five – Mercury, Venus, Mars, Jupiter and Saturn – were all found thousands of years ago, spotted **WANDERING** "randomly" amid the stars. They have been constant features in all human cultures for much of recorded history.

And then nothing else for a long time, at least until the telescope got invented and we could see further than the human eye. Then **GALILEO**

discovered the **four moons** of Jupiter that still bear his name as a group, all seen, reported and confirmed, in a couple of months at the start of 1610. Ganymede, Calisto, Io and Europa. *Basically, Galileo got a telescope, and straight out of the box, discovered four moons that first weekend.* He probably stuck it back in the garage after that and never used it again. WHY BOTHER? JOB DONE.

Next up on the discoveries was the **DUTCH ASTRONOMER, CHRISTIAAN HUYGENS.** In 1655, Huygens discovered a first moon of Saturn, later to be confirmed as its LARGEST MOON, the one we now call Titan (it didn't get that name for another 200 years though).

Here's the other cool thing Huygens did. In 1655, word travelled slowly. **There was no immediate mass media like there is today,** so announcements were made at the pace of letters being hand delivered, across entire countries. It was perfectly possible to send someone a letter about an incredible discovery you had made, and for them to just **steal** the idea and tell you they had already thought of it.

"OH TITAN? YEAH, I SAW THAT AAAAAAGES AGO. DID YOU NOT GET MY LETTER?"

Therefore, to protect their discoveries, scientists would send out an announcement in **code** and only when they knew everyone had heard there was a discovery would they explain how to **decode** the message and find out what the discovery was.

This is what Huygens did. He announced the discovery of Titan with an anagram, sort of like receiving a letter that just said "ROMAN FOOT UNSEWN!" or "A NEW FORUM ON SNOT!" and when he knew it was safe, revealed that the message was actually "**New moon of Saturn!**" all along. His message was a little longer, and in Latin, and when it was decoded it said, "**SATURN'S MOON REVOLVES IN SIXTEEN DAYS, FOUR HOURS**", thus revealing his discovery.

Next up was the **ITALIAN ASTRONOMER, CASSINI**, who spotted four more moons around Saturn between 1672 and 1684, and for his trouble was immortalized in **The Cassini Division**, which sounds like a spy movie, but is actually the **black circle** in the middle of Saturn's rings.

So there were lots of moons being discovered but no planets until ... 1781, when **WILLIAM HERSCHEL** discovered what he thought was a comet and then realized was a planet. He called it "THE GEORGIAN STAR" after Britain's then-king, George III, which was a pretty smart move, even though the planet was eventually renamed after **Uranus, the Greek god of the sky**. Greek gods of the sky don't have jobs to hand out, y'see, but real kings do, and Herschel naming a planet after him was probably why King George invented the job of **King's Astronomer**, just for him. He was pretty good at it, too, discovering even more **moons of Saturn** and making his fortune designing and building telescopes with the help of his sister, Caroline.

WE HAD TO WAIT UNTIL MIDWAY THROUGH THE NEXT CENTURY until another planet made an appearance, and it was in a very indirect way. **THE FRENCH ASTRONOMER ALEXIS BOUVARD** noticed that Uranus was straying from its normal orbit, and he predicted that it was because it was being **dragged away** from its expected path by the gravitational pull of another, previously **undiscovered, planet.** Sadly, he died before the existence of this eighth planet was confirmed, but two other astronomers, **URBAIN LE VERRIER** and **JOHN COUCH ADAMS**, independently used his work to predict where this `mystery object` should be. Then, on the night of 23 September 1846,

Johann Galle pointed the telescope of the Berlin Observatory at the section of sky Le Verrier had indicated and, within a degree of the prediction, UP POPPED NEPTUNE.

There was some controversy about **who should get credit for the discovery**, but it showed that planet-finding was getting more difficult. We were **more likely** to discover a planet because of noticing its effect on things around it, than just by spotting one with a telescope. But most of all, it showed that anagrams are the only way to tell people big news. As I always say, **NASA ARMOR FROG AHOY**! I mean, HOORAY FOR ANAGRAMS!

Should we mention **POOR OLD PLUTO HERE?**
I mean, it was a planet when it got discovered, back
in 1930. And it **DID** get discovered because people
noticed that something **mysterious** was making
both Uranus and Neptune **WOBBLE** off their expected
paths. This is what planetary discovery was turning
into: look at something you already know and see if it
behaves slightly unexpectedly. Like when you're going for
a walk and then you suddenly think, "**Where has the
dog gone?**" and you turn and look back and wobble
a bit off the path. It seemed that both Uranus and
Neptune kept glancing over their shoulder at something,
and then astronomers looked really carefully and
found **Pluto**.

Of course, Pluto isn't technically
a planet any more but even
if we include it, you can see
we were only discovering a
new planet once every hundred

years. And it's nearly a hundred years since Pluto. So, how many planets are we on now? Nine? Ten? Maybe a dozen?

Let's see how many we have discovered so far. A quick check on the computer ... The total is ... our eight planets and ...

4,260 other planets, across 3,146 solar systems.

WHOA!

What happened?

We discovered **exoplanets**, that's what happened.

A FARAWAY FIND

An **EXOPLANET** is any planet outside our Solar System. It was always presumed that other stars apart from our Sun might have planetary systems around them, but it was also presumed that they would be far too far away to see with any telescope. The next nearest star to Earth, Proxima Centauri, is **forty trillion kilometres away**, or **30,000 times further away than the Sun**.

However, we've already seen that while a planet might be faint to the point of being `invisible`, you can still see its effect on planets nearby, like the missing dog we talked about above. Would a planet have the same effect on a star? Would a planet we couldn't see make a star wobble and give itself away?

As it turns out yes, they would. But the wobble would be very small, just the sign of a giant star shifting ever

51 PEGASI

so slightly off its
centre of gravity because of
a much smaller orbiting planet.

In 1995, the astronomers Michel Mayor
and Didier Queloz discovered that tell-tale
WOBBLE in the motion of a star called **51 PEGASI**.
It is the fifty-first star listed in that constellation, and
by pure coincidence lies **fifty-one light years away
from us**. You can see it on a clear night. It's in the
constellation **PEGASUS**, although not one of the stars
that define the constellation. It's about midway down
the front of Pegasus's "chest". If you do see it, give it a
wave. Around that star orbits the first planet we ever

discovered outside our Solar System. Don't expect
a wave back though. The planet is officially called **51
PEGASI B**, but was quickly (and unofficially) named
Bellerophon, after the ancient Greek hero who rode
Pegasus, although probably not while sitting halfway up
its chest. The name was later changed to **DIMIDIUM**.

Anyway, life wouldn't be easy on Dimidium. For a start, it is **huge**, about half the size of Jupiter – so much, much **bigger than Earth** – and, very surprisingly, it sits even closer to its sun than Mercury does to ours.

If you remember all that stuff earlier in the book about how our Solar System was made, you'll recall that the **BIG PLANETS TEND TO BE FURTHER OUT**, after the star had grabbed most of the **LOOSE DUST AND BLOWN THE LIGHT GASES AWAY**. Do you remember all that? Of course you do. We thought that would be the way all solar systems got made, but it turns out, things are **WEIRDER IN SPACE**. A planet that size **just shouldn't** be sitting so close to the star. **And weirder was to follow.**

HUNTING FOR NEW PLANETS

First though, let's find another way to hunt planets. When a planet passes in front of a star, it tends to block out some of the light of the star. That is one way we spot faraway planets. **You wait for the light to dim just a tiny little bit.** And then you wait to see if it happens again. And then you wait the same amount of time and see if it happens yet again. If it keeps happening at the same interval, then you have a planet, in orbit, regularly looping around its sun.

What is the simplest way to demonstrate this? Easy. Find a desk lamp and switch it on. **Oh no!** You weren't looking straight at it, were you? **DON'T EVER DO THAT!**

Right, now step two: blink rapidly and look away while your eyes recover from staring at a desk lamp as it was being switched on. Now you have to wait while that weird white shadow burnt on to your eyeballs calms down.

Total diversion! That weird white shadow is called an **AFTER-IMAGE**! I just looked it up and found loads of great optical illusions. No time for that here but look it up sometime!

Right, let's start again.

Try it again with **a slightly dimmer desk lamp**. Good. Never speak of the first desk lamp again.

TURN ON THE LAMP. THIS IS THE STAR.

NOW TRAIN A SMALL BEE TO FLY IN TINY CIRCLES AROUND THE LAMP. Look, I haven't got the space here to explain how to train a bee to give up its life of collecting nectar and making honey and hanging out with all the other bees, in order to lead a lonely life with you, flying round and round a lamp demonstrating how planets work, but you'll work something out. Maybe offer it some sugar water.

Anyway, look at the lamp as the bee goes in front of it at regular intervals. Do you see the way the light dims, just a tiny amount? When the bee flies around the back of the lamp, the light goes back to normal and when the bee comes out in front, the light dims yet again. **Can you see that?**

No, of course you can't.

The difference is way **too small** for us to see with the naked eye. And if you imagine a planet passing in front of a star, the difference is miniscule, sometimes as little as one-hundredth of one per cent of the normal **BRIGHTNESS** of the star. So it is even more impossible for us to see. But that's OK, because we use incredibly delicate and sensitive cameras to detect the tiny drop in light. We even send cameras into space, so they won't be interrupted by the **dust and clouds** and difference in temperatures that make light **WOBBLE** in our atmosphere.

In 2009, we launched a special camera called Kepler into space to look for planets. It was so fine-tuned that we had to use liquid helium to cool it and make it **super-duper sensitive** (a technical term, used by actual scientists all the time). **LIQUID HELIUM COOLS TO -269 DEGREES CELSIUS** and allows the instruments to measure the dip in light in 150,000 stars. If you want to see what Kepler was looking at go out and find the constellation of **Cygnus the swan**. If you imagine the swan flying up the sky, Kepler was looking at an area around the tip of its right wing. All 150,000 stars were there. Give them a wave. Now, here, you have a much better chance of getting a wave back.

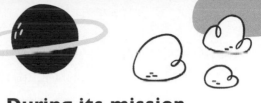

During its mission
Kepler discovered (at last count)
2,392 planets and there are another 2,400
waiting to be confirmed. It was a massive
success. It discovered Earth-like planets, Jupiter-like gas
giants, and planets at all sorts of temperatures ranging
from -220 degrees Celsius, all the way up to poor
WASP-12B, which has the dubious honour of being
the planet closer to its star than any other. **It's fourteen**
times nearer its star than Mercury is to the Sun and
the surface temperature is 2,200 degrees Celsius. It's
so close that the star's gravity is turning the entire
planet oval, like a rugby ball, as the planet is pulled out
of shape. You can add the inhabitants of WASP-12b to
the list of "**people we're not expecting to hear from**".

Kepler's brilliant mission finished in
2018, when it ran out of the super-cold
helium gas. Its reward for doing such a fantastic job

is to float in space staring at the stars. It trails behind Earth in an orbit round the Sun, but in a slightly slower, wider orbit than ours. In 2060, we will almost catch up with it, like lapping the slower runner round a running track, but Earth's gravity will pull poor Kepler, long retired, down into a closer, faster orbit, so it will speed away from us, like a **sneaky runner** who you thought was slower, but switched to the inside lane and got faster. **THEN IT WILL SPEND FIFTY-SEVEN YEARS SLOWLY CATCHING UP** with us, but when it gets too close... **YES, YOU GUESSED IT** – our gravity will lift it into the older, wider slower orbit it had before. And this whole silly to-and-fro race will go on for ever.

SPEAKING OF THINGS GOING ON FOR EVER – THE BEE?! Is that

bee still flying round your desk lamp? Give it some sugar water and let it go back to its hive. The poor thing must be exhausted.

That bee and the Kepler Satellite. Two great heroes of science.

Kepler has now been succeeded by TESS, the Transiting Exoplanet Survey Satellite, launched in 2018, and the discoveries continue.

I SHALL CALL YOU PLANET BooBoo BEE DooP. NEXT!

SOME EXCITING DISCOVERIES

There are some amazing planets and solar systems we have found and I'm going to found and I'm going to mention a few of them. Unfortunately, with this many new discoveries happening so fast, we haven't had time to invent cool names for them all. If I get bored of writing things like Planet HD **80606 B**, and start making up names, don't presume those are the real names. **They haven't let me officially name the planets, yet.**

But if you could choose a new place to live, how about these as candidates?

A planet with two suns!

Do you remember that bit in *Star Wars* where Luke Skywalker stares across the desert, in a mopey way, while the two suns of Tatooine slowly set? Well, every scientist in the world remembers that scene. **And they ALL want to find Tatooine.**

And lots of them have. **There are, at last count, fifty-one planets in solar systems with two suns.** Mainly the planet orbits the big star, but sometimes it orbits the smaller star instead. Sometimes, the two stars spin round each other, and the planet is further out orbiting them both at the same time. Just try to work out how many different ways they could see eclipses. TOI **13388** is a good example. It's about seven times bigger than Earth, and it orbits a large sun ten per cent bigger than ours and a second sun about a third of our Sun's mass. It sees a solar eclipse every fifteen days! You'd almost get bored of seeing solar eclipses! **I shall call this planet EclipseyJoe!**

But how about a planet with three suns?

We can find you one of those as well! If you travel 149 light years away, into the Cygnus constellation, and stand on the surface of HD 188753 (or one of its moons – it's mainly gas) you'll see three stars orbiting each other. I shall call it TripleyMary!

And how about a planet with four suns?

Guess what? We've found that as well. **KEPLER-64B** (also called **PH1**) is larger than Neptune, another **GAS GIANT**, and it orbits a double star every 137 days, while another double star, about ninety billion miles away, orbits the whole lot of them. It got the name **PH1** because it was the first star ever discovered by amateur astronomers visiting **PlanetHunters.org**, a website that takes the unexamined Kepler data and lets anyone search through it to find a planet. **The planet was named in their honour, but I shall call it QuadrupleyBob!**

Any with water?

An excellent question because, let's face it, water is really useful for life and that's ultimately what we're looking for here. In the constellation of Leo, 110 light years away, we have found water vapour in the atmosphere of **PLANET K2-18B**, or **CloudySusan, as I shall call it**. CloudySusan is in the Goldilocks Zone, but its star is a pretty radioactive one, which isn't a great help for life. Plus, since it's eight times larger than Earth, gravity would be **eight times stronger**, so anything living there would have to have really strong thighs just to walk around. **So, big-legged aliens only on CloudySusan.**

WHAT'S THE NEAREST ONE?

Well, you can't get any nearer than our nearest star, **PROXIMA CENTAURI,** a "mere" 4.2 light years away (40 trillion kilometres). And swooping round that star, once every eleven days, is the rocky planet of **PROXIMA B.** About 1.3 times the size of Earth, it is the closest exoplanet to Earth, and if we could find a way to shield ourselves from the amazing amounts of **RADIATION** coming off that star of theirs, we'd be able to go and visit them in only… hmm, quite a long time actually. We might come back to that question a little later.

JUST LIKE HOME

But it does naturally lead to the key query about exoplanets, which is:

WHAT ABOUT ONE LIKE EARTH? IS THERE ONE OF THOSE?

Depending on what you mean by "like Earth", yes, there are already loads of good candidates. There is even a measure of how "Earth-like" a planet is, running from **zero to one**, based on its size and surface temperature, among other things. Earth obviously scores one on the scale, but **there are sixteen known exoplanets with scores above 0.8**. The highest is KOI-4878.01 with an **EARTH SIMILARITY INDEX (ESI)** of 0.98, which is great, but it's more than 1,000 light years away, so even if we sent a message at the speed of light, it would be more than two thousand years until we got a reply. Proxima b, that nearest exoplanet mentioned just now, has a score of 0.87.

The most interesting direction to point our telescopes might be towards the **TRAPPIST-1 star** in the constellation of **Aquarius**. TRAPPIST-1 has a system of seven planets, three of them in the "**GOLDILOCKS**" **HABITABLE ZONE**, and two of them are in the top ten most Earth-like planets. The most exciting is **TRAPPIST-1e**, a little smaller than Earth, and spinning round its star in a year of only six Earth-days.

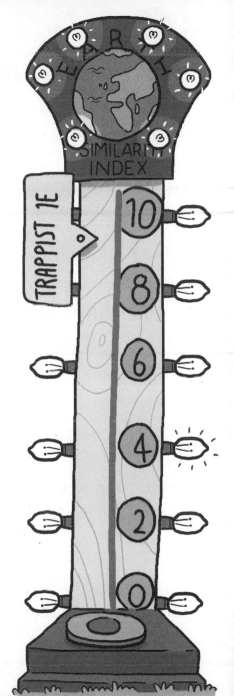

TRAPPIST-1e is tidally locked, which means one side faces the star all the time, and the other is permanently in darkness. If there is life there, it probably lives in the boundary area between **LIGHT** and **DARK** where the temperatures are best for liquid water. Could you imagine growing up on a planet where it's always dark in one direction and always bright in the other? Where a year is only 146 HOURS LONG and there are no days and nights? You'd certainly save money on curtains, at least for one side of the house.

TRAPPIST-1e is going to be one of the first places at which NASA will point the new **James Webb Telescope** when it is launched. The James

Webb is designed to look at the **EXOPLANETS** we've already seen, but analyse the light around the planets to see if they have an `atmosphere` and, if so, what gases they're made of.

This is a great example of science working with the very, very **tiny** to tell you something about the very, very **huge**. In fact, this is so amazing, it's worth taking a couple of moments to explain **why** it's so amazing.

FROM TEENY TINY TO MEGA HUGE

Atoms are pretty small, right?
Tiny building blocks of nature, like their own little solar systems, with **HEAVY NEUTRONS** and **PROTONS** in the middle and `tiny, light electrons` floating in a cloud around them. The electrons are VERY HAPPY in that cloud, a certain distance away from the big heavy nucleus. **They can only move away from that "orbit" if they absorb exactly the right amount of energy to get out to the next orbit, and that exact amount is like a "SIGNATURE" of which atom they are.**

I'M HAPPY HERE, BUT GIVE ME THE EXACT RIGHT AMOUNT OF ENERGY AND I'LL JUMP... TO HERE

So, let's say you have a cloud of gas, and you shine a light through it. The light is made of particles of light, called "**PHOTONS**" and they will be of all different amounts of **energy**, depending on their **WAVELENGTHS**. When the light passes through the gas, and all the atoms in the gas, it might just happen that some of those photons have **EXACTLY** the amount of energy the electrons are looking for.

The photons' energy will get **ABSORBED** by the electrons and the electrons will **jump** from their usual distance from the nucleus to an "orbit" further out.

YES, HERE WE GO!

THIS IS VERY EXCITING for the electrons, but they really aren't supposed to be all the way out there, **so pretty quickly the electron dumps this extra energy**, and drops back again to its usual place. But the beam of light we should be seeing is now missing all the photons of one particular **WAVELENGTH**. They all got stolen by the electrons so they could jump to a different orbit.

Can you imagine anything tinier happening? Teeny, tiny jumps involving teeny, tiny bits of energy. **BUT HERE'S THE AMAZING THING.** We can see that it happened. We can point a telescope **at a star trillions of miles away**, and the light of that star passes through the gases in the atmosphere of an exoplanet. **It makes the electrons in that atmosphere dance**, so that some photons of light get absorbed and aren't in the light when it reaches us. And when I say "reaches us", it is worth stressing the amazing journey the light takes

to get to us anyway: the photons have travelled these
HUGE ENORMOUS DISTANCES, maybe trillions
of miles, across all of empty space, just to land on a
camera, in a telescope, that we launched into space to
look for planets.

When we look at the light we receive, we
can see which bits are missing.

And we know they are
missing because they
were **grabbed** by
electrons.

And we know that
electrons only take very
specific ones, depending
on which **MOLECULE**
they happen to land in.

WE'RE HERE!
WELL MOST OF US ARE HERE!

And so we can tell, because of this **tiny, tiny dance** the electrons do, what gases there are in the atmosphere. **It's the tiniest thing**, telling us the **HUGEST THINGS**. We can tell if there is oxygen for breathing, or water in the clouds, or gases of hydrogen or helium, or **MURDEROUS SULPHURIC ACID**, or a million other things. We can even spot the signatures of gases that nature cannot make, like the sort of gases we have made to run fridges for years, called **chlorofluorocarbons (CFCs)**, that only exist because we designed and built them in factories.

We have the technology to see gases that only exist because intelligent creatures made them.

If some day we look at the light from a distant **EXOPLANET**, and we see the distinct, unmistakable signature of one of those "**MANUFACTURED**" **GASES**, then we will know, for sure, **100 per cent** definitely, that this is a planet that did, and maybe could still, harbour life as intelligent as us.

It would be the greatest discovery in science, and it would have happened because electrons like to jump.

From the very tiny, **TO THE VERY HUGE**.

And while we recover from how great that is, we will face another question about the alien life we have just discovered.

SHOULD WE TRY AND COMMUNICATE WITH THEM?

So, we've found a likely candidate for a planet full of new space friends. Let's go and meet them! How long might that possibly take?

It will take a long, long, long time.

Let's pick our nearest candidate from all those exoplanets, **PROXIMA B**. It orbits the next nearest sun to Earth, Proxima Centauri, and sits a mere 4.2 light years away.

That's a manageable little hop, right?

4.2 light years away means that it would take a beam of light 4.2 years to get there. **The speed of light is the fastest thing in the Universe**, and when we travel, we don't go anywhere near the speed of light. **We can't because we have mass. We're made of stuff. We have weight, so it**

takes energy to get us moving and even more energy to get us moving faster and faster. Ultimately, we couldn't get up to the speed of light because it would take impossible amounts of energy to keep accelerating us. The closer we get to the speed of light, the more difficult we are to accelerate, while **light zips along** happily at top speed, because it doesn't weigh anything.

So we won't get there in 4.2 years. What's the bad news, eh? How long will it take?

Well ... would you be happy with 20,000 years?

Yep, we're a LOT slower than light.

ONE LAP OF THE TRACK - 3, 2, 1, GO!

I'VE ALREADY FINISHED!

HOW FAST CAN WE GO?

The fastest humans have ever travelled was during the Apollo 10 mission in 1969. Apollo 10 was the final test mission before the Moon landing made by Apollo 11, and the mission was to fly to the Moon, launch the lunar lander, descend to just nine miles above the surface and then ... come home, without landing. **Ouch!**

Obviously this made perfect sense at the time. Each Apollo mission was a further test of what was possible, and another step towards the **ultimate goal of sending astronauts to the Moon and getting them home.** The lunar lander had to be tested, and they needed to see it could recombine and return to Earth, without the extra complication of the Moon landing and take-off.

But, still...

I mean, this is a journey anyone would be **AMAZED** to make, and a greater journey than any human had ever made at the time, and remains greater than any journey anyone has made since 1972. If they offered any of us a journey all the way to the Moon and then to skim nine miles over the surface, we'd bite their hands off for it. It would be the trip of a lifetime! It would be a sight only seen by twenty-four other people in history! **But, still ...** you'd want to walk on the Moon. You've come all this way! Plus, you know that the very next flight is the one that walks on the Moon. **History will for ever remember the name Neil Armstrong, and not Thomas P. Stafford**, the captain of Apollo 10, and the only man on that mission who didn't get to return to the Moon on a later trip. So, Thomas P. Stafford, you get this claim to fame instead (alongside a career as an astronaut, and test pilot who flew over 120 different types of aeroplanes and three different spaceships).

YOU ARE THE FASTEST HUMAN BEING IN HISTORY (alongside crewmates John Young and Eugene Cernan)!

On its return from the Moon, Apollo 10 hit speeds of 39,897 km/h (24,791 miles per hour). That sounds pretty fast, doesn't it? You'd get from London to Sydney in twenty-six minutes at that speed, although you'd be hard pressed to recognize the Opera House as it went whooshing past your window. And how long would that fastest human speed of all time take us to get to Proxima Centauri, our nearest star?

114,155 YEARS.

This will not be a quick trip.

STUCK IN ORBIT

Spaceships can go faster now, of course. That speed record was set more than fifty years ago, and the only reason astronauts haven't travelled any faster since is because they haven't gone very far since then, and where they go has **a very definite speed limit**. Since the Moon landings, all journeys into space have been to orbits around Earth and those are surprisingly close. **The International Space Station is in an orbit only 400 kilometres (250 miles) above Earth.** It isn't stationary though. To stay in orbit, the Space Station has to travel at a very specific speed so as to be constantly "**FALLING**" around the Earth. That way, it keeps from ever being pulled down to Earth by gravity, and can stay "falling" in orbit for ever. All the satellites you hear about – spy satellites, GPS satellites, the ones that deliver us football matches – they all have a very specific speed they have to travel at, to keep them in their orbit.

For the ISS, 400 kilometres above us, that speed is 27,580 km/h. All the time, the Space Station is flying that fast over the Earth. This means it travels an entire orbit of the Earth in just ninety minutes.

Some people **(parents usually, they aren't great at this stuff)** think that if a craft is travelling that fast, the astronauts inside must be **SQUISHED BACK** in their seats all the time, like when the car speeds up and you get pushed back. It's not the speed that makes you get squeezed back in your seat though, it's the change in speed – the **acceleration.** That's because it takes force to change something's speed, and when the speed isn't changing, you don't feel any force, **so no matter what your speed is, you don't get squished back in your seat.**

TRY THIS: place a friend, a brother or a sister, a pet, or a large metal safe into a **supermarket trolley** and then push the trolley to make it move.

YOU HAVE TO SHOVE HARD TO START THE TROLLEY MOVING

— that's the **force**, and riders can feel it shoving into their back — but once they've started moving, they can maintain their speed with no push at all. OK, they do slow down — we all know that — **but that's because of friction between the wheels and the ground, mainly, so here's a better version of this experiment**.

What are you doing with that safe?

Science...

Take your friend, brother or sister, pet or a large metal safe to a **slidey, frozen lake**, and put them in a shopping trolley and give them a shove. **AWAY THEY GO**, after you've accelerated them, and they'll maintain that speed until something puts force on them to **stop**, most likely a tree on the other side of the lake. Being stopped is also a change in speed, so it needs force to happen again, just in the opposite direction.

FOR ORBITING ASTRONAUTS, the acceleration comes during the launch, when the rocket takes off and there is clearly quite a lot of force being placed on them. So much force, in fact, that they can feel as much as three times heavier than normal pressed into their seats during the take-off. Imagine sitting on a chair, and then having another you lie on top, and then **ANOTHER** you on top again. It's tough to breathe and very difficult to move. But after a few minutes, something quite magical happens.

When they reach orbit, and that **magical speed of 27,580 km/h**, the astronauts then start their journey of "falling" constantly round the Earth and then, amazingly … there's no force at all on them! **THEY START TO FLOAT!** They aren't accelerating, either because of a rocket pushing them, or because gravity is dragging them down. They are constantly free-falling, so they feel no force at all, not even gravity, and they float, weightlessly.

The change is quite dramatic and sometimes very uncomfortable. A lot of astronauts suffer badly from nausea and vomiting for the first few days of being in this unnatural state. That settles down, and as they grow accustomed to their new home, other more long-term health issues become more important.

SPENDING TIME IN SPACE

A lot of studies have been done on living long-term in space. As we've seen, a journey to even our nearest star will take many, many years. The greatest amount of time anyone has ever spent in space, in total, is **879 days**, by Russian cosmonaut Genady Padalka, spread over five different missions, usually about six months each. Peggy Whitson holds the NASA record, with 665 days, spread over three missions. **The longest single space mission was by Valery Polyakov, who spent 438 days on the Mir Space Station, from January 1994 until March 1995.**

These are all huge achievements, of course. But they wouldn't get us very far on the road to Proxima Centauri. In fact, they wouldn't even get us to Mars and back. The flight time to Mars, our nearest neighbour, is expected to be about six to eight months, depending on where the planets

are in their orbits. You'd presume we would like to spend a little time there, after such a long journey, and then another six to eight months on the journey home. **Therefore a Mars mission would be about three years long**, and about half of that would be spent in weightlessness.

HERE'S WHAT MIGHT HAPPEN TO THE BODY OVER THREE YEARS IN SPACE.

You'd be weightless for the journey, which sounds great, but our bodies are used to constantly working against **gravity**. Our muscles and bones fight against it all the time, particularly when we have to get up for school, or to do tidying, when gravity is especially strong — something that parents were never taught in school, but we now know for certain.

If you spend months and months **TRAVELLING WEIGHTLESSLY**, you have to exercise constantly, maybe two hours every day, just to keep those muscles and bones strong. It's necessary for your heart too. In normal life, it's pumping blood all the time, all round your body and back again, so it's also working against gravity. **Remove the gravity and you take away that constant effort.** Your heart might weaken over time and simply not be strong enough when you get home.

SO, LOTS OF TIME ON A TREADMILL.

After an orbiting space station, the next destination as we travel into space would be a return to the Moon. There we could test the technology for living on different planets and start experimenting with **mining**, although for very different reasons to mining on Earth. The most precious substance we could find on the Moon would not be gold or diamonds, but **PLAIN OLD WATER**. "Water is the oil of Space", as one scientist put it. It can be used for drinking, obviously, and washing and flushing toilets and filling water pistols and all the other stuff we use water for normally, but water is made of hydrogen and oxygen, and if we can separate them, we can use the oxygen for breathing and the hydrogen for **ROCKET FUEL**. If we could source enough water on the Moon, we could use it as a low-gravity launch pad for rockets into **deep space**.

NASA, the European Space Agency, Russia, China and Japan have all supported a proposal to build a space station, like the ISS, but in orbit around the Moon, sometime in the 2020s.

We could also find water on comets, which are usually described as "**dirty snowballs**", as they are made up of frozen water, methane, carbon dioxide and other ices, all mixed up with rock and dust. If you could land on one it would be like a **refuelling station** for your rocket, **plus, it would be unbelievably cool to just land on a comet and that's important too**.

Next stop on the journey into space might be **MARS**.
As we've said, this would be a three-year mission
and currently there are no plans to send humans to
Mars, as all the **robots** and rovers we're sending
are doing such a good job instead. This is a pity, since
on Mars the gravity is one-third of Earth's so you
would have **super-strength** for a while
– YAY! – until your body starting getting used to
having less work to do and, again, you started getting
weaker – BOO!

Another long-term health problem on a trip to the **RED PLANET** would be having to retrain your balance and co-ordination each time you change environment – transitioning from Earth's gravity to weightlessness, to the weaker gravity of Mars, back to weightlessness for the journey home and then, as a punchline, back to the full gravity of Earth again, when you are all weak and **WOBBLY**.

When astronauts return to Earth after six months onboard the **ISS**, they can hardly stand up at first, since the gravity is so strange and **overpowering** for them. If you see a photo of an ISS crew landing back on Earth, the astronauts and cosmonauts are always sitting in **DECKCHAIRS** smiling weakly. It's all they have the strength for.

LONG-DISTANCE JOURNEYS

Three years is just how long it will take us to get to Mars and back. Earlier in the book we spoke about the ice moons: Europa, around Jupiter, and Enceladus, around Saturn, possibly our nearest best-candidates for life in the SOLAR SYSTEM.

Both **Enceladus** and **Europa** have vast seas of water underneath a shell of ice. Surely we could land there, tap on the ice and see who answers? **How difficult would that be?**

Well, there's the distance again. Jupiter is "only" three years away, but because it is such a huge beast of a planet, it pulls all sorts of stuff into orbit around it, including loads and **loads** of **radioactive-charged particles**. Europa is an insanely dangerous place to land unless you are driving a big thick, lead-covered rocket and they are even heavier and slower than normal rockets. Plus, we suspect there may be **GIANT SPIKES OF ICE** on the surface, as tall as a five-storey building, making any landing there, as NASA would surely put it, "**A BIT OUCHY**".

Saturn is even further out. We sent the *Cassini* mission there and it took **seven years** to arrive. The only way to do such a long journey without needing a load of fuel was to "slingshot" around Jupiter, where the **spacecraft** flies close to the huge planet, gets briefly caught by its gravity, and then **flung** out behind it at greater speed. It's like if you roller-skated past a merry-

go-round, held on to the bars for a second and then let go and got thrown out **EVEN FASTER**.

It's a brilliant technique for cheap space travel, but you need Saturn and Jupiter to be in **JUST** the right position, and that only happens **once every twenty years**. It happened in 2000, which is why we launched *Cassini* in 1997 just to reach Jupiter in time. Our next window is **2037**, to meet Jupiter in 2040. If you miss that bus (like we did in 2020 – we had no mission ready to go in 2017), you have to wait a fair while until the next one.

You have got to be kidding!

NEXT iN 20 YEARS

LET'S SPEED THIS UP!

Everything is such a long way away, so shouldn't we try to make the rockets faster? Well, rockets have sped up a fair bit in the last fifty years. The fastest non-crewed spacecraft is the **NASA Parker Solar Probe,** which reached nearly 247,000 km/h (six times faster than Apollo 10) while also holding the record for being the closest we have ever been to the Sun. The mission is expected to get within **FOUR MILLION MILES** of the Sun in 2024, and at that heat, you'd want to be able to get away pretty fast. Obviously, this isn't a crewed mission, but if we could make a habitable spacecraft that fast, it would get the journey time to Proxima Centauri down to a manageable …

18,486 YEARS.

One way to make the journey would be to create a **multigenerational mission**.

You build a huge, huge **spaceship**, with the ability to grow food, and recirculate water and air, and then fill it with people willing to live their lives, and have all of their children live **THEIR** lives, journeying to another star system. **And they do this for hundreds, maybe thousands of years.**

You might not even need as many people as you'd think. Two French scientists tried to work out a **formula** for how many people would be required to keep a ship going **INDEFINITELY**. Even allowing for the occasional crash, explosion, or outbreak of plague, they estimated that **NINETY-EIGHT PEOPLE** – forty-nine sets of parents – would be enough to keep a ship going all the way to Proxima Centauri. That would be like all the parents and kids from your class in school going. **Imagine that group, all piled into a spaceship for nearly 20,000 years**.

But I don't want to be a dentist!

The ship would still have to be big enough to feature **bio-domes and green spaces**, to grow food, accommodate animals and the changing human populations. You would always need to have people trained as doctors, dentists and mechanics and all the essential jobs, so there might be a lot of ordering people about. **It might not be a happy ship.** Plus, it's not like there is anything to see out of the window. Once we leave the Solar System, we don't go past anywhere interesting until we get all the way to **Proxima** so it's a pretty dull, empty journey.

The greatest difficulty might not be building the ship, but keeping everyone excited about the mission for a few thousand years.

After a while, you'll have a crew who have never seen Earth, and they might just decide to turn the ship around and go home instead. And could you blame them? We don't even know whether Proxima has ice cream, or waterparks, or anything.

It might be easier if you could make the entire crew **HIBERNATE FOR THE JOURNEY**. The European Space Agency have investigated this, not least because if you remove all the living space, the ship can be much `smaller` and `lighter` and need far less fuel to get to higher speeds. You would need to carry a lot less food and supplies. Sleeping people eat a lot less, although they will want a **HUUUGE** breakfast when they get up.

WHEN A BEAR HIBERNATES, IT REDUCES ITS METABOLISM, its internal engine, by about

seventy-five per cent. Humans are not built to hibernate, of course, but there are times where it has been safer to knock a human out for medical reasons, during an operation, obviously, but sometimes after an accident patients have been placed in a form of hypothermia, a rapid cooling of the body, in order to slow the metabolism and buy time until proper medical help can be given. The longest anyone

has been in this artificial state is two weeks. Doctors have placed patients in long-term comas, but – again – rarely for more than a fortnight.

Here's one **advantage** of hibernation though. Just like bears do, it would be advisable for humans to stock up on reserves of food before the hibernation. Astronauts are usually quite slim and super-fit. A hibernating astronaut would be allowed a lot more **CHOCOLATE** and could even claim it was necessary for the journey. They were already excited about reaching Proxima Centauri. Now they get to pig out first. It's a double win.

COULD ROBOTS GO INSTEAD?

A slightly **CRAZIER IDEA** would be to upload your brain into a **ROBOT, OR A CYBORG**, and then send that on a spaceship for 18,486 years. There would be **no need for food or drink**, or constant exercise. And a robot could arrive on a planet of vastly different gravity, **radiation** and atmosphere and be ready to go immediately. The only problem is that we can't actually take a **SNAPSHOT** of our brains yet. There are companies who claim to be able to **FREEZE A HUMAN BRAIN** intact, and then, maybe at some later stage, defrost it and recover the brain. The **TEENY-TINY PROBLEM** with this, and I don't even know why I'm mentioning it, since it is such an itsy-bitsy problem — **the process is 100 per cent fatal and that's the end of you**. I think I'd even take the boring **18,486-YEAR JOURNEY** over that.

Wish you were here!

Instead, we could send a robot with an **ARTIFICIAL INTELLIGENCE BRAIN** as our ambassador. It would communicate with the locals and send us back their responses. It would have all the advantages of robots in this situation, plus it could react in a human way to these **new civilizations**. But that's doesn't feel like the meeting you were promised, right? You actually want to be the one shaking the tentacles of an alien beast. Not the one getting an email **POSTCARD** from a robot, using your brain, to make friends on the other side of the **GALAXY**.

A WEIRDER WAY TO TRAVEL

So let's try something even more totally wild and unlikely then. There must be a way of crossing vast distances quickly. They've done it in enough films! Let's take this ship to hyperspace! **LET'S ACTIVATE THE WARP-DRIVE!** When are we getting some of that technology, eh?

Well ... we could try opening a "**WORMHOLE**" in space, using a **black hole** to bend space and time so much that you link two parts of the galaxy with a doorway between them. The thought is that a black hole would bend space and time so much, that different parts of it would meet up, and there would be a path, or a "wormhole", between the two points. That would allow for instantaneous travel and was for a long time though to be **THEORETICALLY POSSIBLE**, which is a Big Science word for, "It **MIGHT** work, but don't pin your hopes on it."

Black holes are the single most amazing and destructive things in the Universe. They are created when the mass of an entire star collapses under its own weight into a single point of **incredible density**.

Imagine all the mass of a star SQUEEZED on to the tiniest point on the tip of your finger. It wouldn't stay on your fingertip for long though. **WHOOSH!** It would suck you straight in as well. The gravitational pull is incredible. Even light cannot escape it. You can shine light on to a black hole, but nothing will bounce back. **This means they are totally black, hence the name.**

Anything passing near them will also get sucked in by their gravity. **A black hole will happily eat an entire galaxy, let alone a single spaceship.** So it's a pretty wild idea to use them as a doorway.

Also, as you can imagine, creating a black hole in order to tear a new hole in the very fabric of space would require a lot of effort. The physicist **KIP THORNE** estimated that to make a three-foot hole would need the same amount of energy as **VAPORIZING JUPITER**. That's if we make it ourselves. A wormhole might also appear due to a naturally occurring black hole, connecting it to another black hole, like **secret tunnels**, or shortcuts, appearing in space. We have a black hole at the centre of our galaxy, and while we haven't seen any evidence of a wormhole behind it yet, we're checking.

Another alternative might be to "fold" space and time, rather than ripping it. In 1994, a Mexican physicist called **MIGUEL ALBUCIERRE** came up with the idea of the "Alcubierre Warp Drive"; a theoretical engine that would place a spaceship in a **"WARP BUBBLE"**, untouched by the rest of the Universe. That way it could ride a "wave" that COMPRESSED SPACE in front of it and **expanded** it behind. The teeny-tiny problem here is that nobody knows how to make a "warp bubble" and nobody is sure how, even if you could make one, you would then get out of it, into the rest of space.

BUT IT WOULD BE FAST! And the other option takes 18,486 years.

Those are the choices, then: get **SQUEEZED** through a black hole, have a really **long** sleep in an **ICE BUCKET**, or take a journey your great-great-great... **grandkids** might get to finish.

And that isn't the end of our problems. Even if we get all the way to our new alien friends, what are we going to say to them?

Deep in space...

MILKY WAY

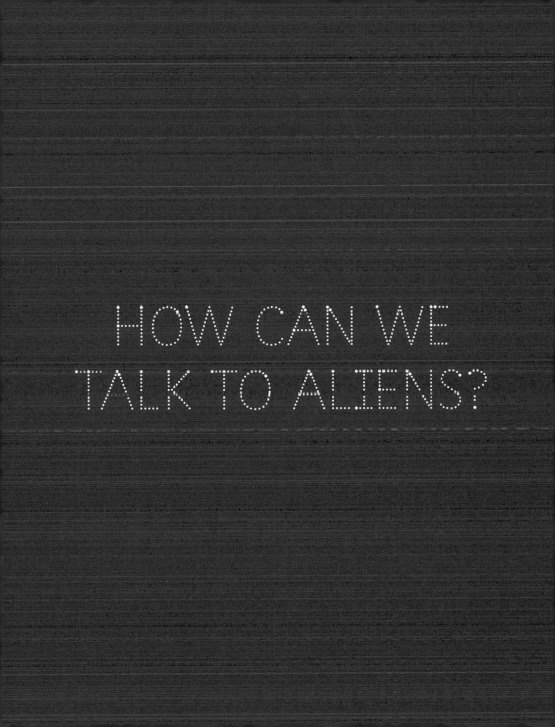

HOW CAN WE TALK TO ALIENS?

We've been trying to talk to aliens for years, of course. Usually through presuming that they were almost just like us, and quite close by. In the 1820s, the mathematician **CARL FRIEDRICH GAUSS** (who was incredibly smart, by the way) invented a method of communicating with aliens that just involved **planting huge groves of pines trees in the Siberian wilderness**, but in the shape of a right-angled triangle, with squares on each side. Gauss reckoned that aliens looking down on us would see the triangles, recognize **PYTHAGORAS'S THEOREM** (or whatever they called it on their planet), think that it was pretty unlikely that these triangles would just appear naturally and that this was **EVIDENCE OF INTELLIGENT LIFE ON EARTH**.

Of course, if aliens can see these **giant triangles** of pine trees, they could probably see all the **cities of the world**, including the one in Germany where Gauss himself lived, and work out that there

THE SQUARE OF THE HIPPOPOTAMUS IS TWICE THE SQUARE OF THE ICE CREAM. OH WHAT IS IT AGAIN?

was intelligent life here from that. There is also some debate over whether it was Gauss who proposed this, although he definitely suggested building **100 GIANT MIRRORS AND BOUNCING SUNLIGHT ON TO THE MOON AS A "SIGNAL TO OUR NEAR NEIGHBOURS"**. If there was somebody on the Moon though, this combination of methods would perfectly recreate the very human experience of sitting bored in a maths class while your teacher goes on about Pythagoras's therorem, and one of your classmates reflects light into your eyes off their watch or pencil case.

Nobody has ever explained why Carl Friedrich Gauss wanted to **IRRITATE** the people of the Moon like this, but he was clearly a messer at school and it's amazing he managed to become a scientist at all.

Other scientists who are just having a laugh include **JOSEPH JOHANN VON LITTROW** of the Vienna Observatory who, in 1840, allegedly proposed **digging a two-mile-long trench in the Sahara desert**, filling it with the **explosive liquid kerosene and then setting fire to it.** You know, for aliens? To send them a message? About life on Earth? Definitely **not** just because it would be cool to light a two-mile-long fire-trench. Again, though, von Littrow wanted the trench to be in a mathematical shape, like Gauss wanted to grow a triangle. **This bit is not a bad idea.**

YES, THE MARSHMALLOWS ARE ALSO FOR THE ALIENS

SENDING MESSAGES WITH SCIENCE

Our greatest problem with extra-terrestrial life will be finding a **common language**, and what will come up again and again in our repeated efforts to contact extra-terrestrials is that scientists on Earth reckon that the scientists on **Kepler 2765-b**, or wherever, while they might not speak any language we can understand, will surely share our knowledge of **BASIC SHAPES AND NUMBERS**.

You might have green skin and four arms, but three is still a PRIME NUMBER. And if you're advanced enough to see the message we're sending you, you'll probably have **spotted** prime numbers while building your version of a telescope. So through history, our messages to space have had a very **SCIENTIFIC** feel to them.

In 1941, the English astronomer **Sir James Jeans** proposed building **A GIANT SEARCHLIGHT** to beam pulses of light in a sequence of prime numbers, as **A BEACON TO SPACE**.

In 1974, a radio message was beamed from the newly upgraded **ARECIBO TELESCOPE IN PUERTO RICO** in the form of a grid of 23 by 79 squares (both primes) that painted a patchwork picture of the telescope, some **DNA**, a little cartoon human figure and our Solar System.

The message was beamed at a collection of stars called the **HERCULES CLUSTER**, which seemed like a good bet, since it contains **hundreds of thousands of stars all clustered together**. It's 21,000 light years away though, **so it might be another 42,000 years before the reply comes back**. Which is a long time to wait if they just send back a cartoon of themselves as well. **Or thank us for the lovely carpet design we sent them.**

Some of our messaging might take even longer than that though. When the space probe **PIONEER 10** launched in 1972 on its mission to visit Jupiter, NASA was well aware that after the fly-by, it would just keep going, on and on, out of the Solar System and into deep space, and that it might be good to leave some sort of **signature** on it, in case it was ever found by other civilizations. To do this, a gold plaque was included in the rocket, with **A NUDE PICTURE OF A MAN AND A WOMAN**, a diagram of the Solar System and directions to our Sun.

TO DO THIS, SCIENTISTS USED PULSARS AS A MAP REFERENCE. Do you remember pulsars from earlier? They are rapidly spinning stars, discovered in a field in Cambridge by Jocelyn Bell Burnell in 1965, but first mistakenly thought to be a message from aliens. Now we know that the pulse they send is regular and unique to them, and therefore we can use them as map references. **In a funny twist, we now include them in the messages we send aliens!**

On the golden plaque, we have shown fourteen different pulsars, and our distance from them. It's a bit of a puzzle, but scientists love puzzles and riddles and hard questions to work out, and the presumption is that alien scientists might be the same.

That said, we only discovered pulsars fifty years ago, so even we couldn't have solved that puzzle until recently. That's the other problem with sending messages to other civilizations: we don't know at what point of their development they'll be.

STARTING THE CONVERSATION

When we raced through the history of life on Earth a little while back, we covered **4.5 BILLION YEARS**. And only in the last fifty did somebody even understand what a pulsar was, unless we have **deeply underestimated the dinosaurs**.

The biggest surprise will be if aliens capture the *Pioneer* spacecraft, find the golden plaque, work out where we are, travel all the way to meet us and then find out that we don't all walk around naked. **What if they were worried we'd be the only ones naked, so to be polite, they arrive naked as well?** They will be so embarrassed when we're dressed and they aren't. **It will be soooo awkward.**

We won't have to deal with that problem for a while though, since *Pioneer 10* isn't due to approach another star system for **two million years.** If the round trip takes four million years, they might even arrive and find some other **CIVILIZATION** here instead of us and that will be awkward too. It would be like knocking on somebody's door and strangers answering

and saying, "**OH NO, THEY DON'T LIVE HERE ANY MORE. THEY MOVED OUT TWO MILLION YEARS AGO.**" Imagine if aliens arrived on Earth tomorrow, looking forward to meeting dinosaurs and we had to break it to them that they were **SIXTY-FIVE MILLION YEARS TOO LATE. And naked. Yet more awkwardness.**

Would aliens even understand the messages we send them? That is a difficult question, and one that involves a lot of guesswork. Even looking at all the strange and diverse forms of life on Earth might not prepare us for what else is out there. We can base our guesswork on a couple of assumptions though.

Aliens will live in the same galaxy as us, so we're sure that they will have the same rules of physics that we have. They will have gravity, electricity and all the forces. The table of elements will be the same, and chemicals will combine in the same way. They will probably get most of their energy from the star at the centre of their **solar system**.

Also, at their most basic, animals will have to do the same stuff they do here: SURVIVE ON THEIR LOCAL ENERGY RESOURCES, TRY NOT TO BECOME FOOD FOR ANOTHER ANIMAL AND HAVE LITTLE ANIMALS. While we can't get into specifics,

we can make some pretty good guesses about how alien animals might have evolved based on the worlds they live in. **EVOLUTION** is the way animals change and develop over millions of years to become more successful at living in their environment. Our evolution is based on a series of chance mutations in our **DNA**, the code in our cells that contains the instructions to build us. **Every time a new generation comes along, the DNA of our parents is copied down and tiny mistakes, mutations and changes are made here and there. Sometimes those mistakes make survival harder and then the change doesn't get passed on.**

Sometimes those mistakes make survival easier and do get passed on. And so, generation after generation, life gets better suited to its environment as well as more diverse and specialized. **WE HAVE NO IDEA IF AN ALIEN LIFE WILL HAVE DNA**, but whatever code they use, they will still probably be under the same pressures as animals here: eat, don't get eaten, have little animals of their own. So, it's pretty likely they will have evolved to suit their environment, and that gives us some **CLUES** as to what form they might take.

Some things are just too useful not to evolve in a particular environment. For example, we live on a planet with a **thick atmosphere**, which is good for flying. So wings would be useful. Which is why wings evolved separately in insects, bats, birds and PTEROSAURS (flying reptiles that took to the skies at the time of the dinosaurs). Those animals aren't related to each other the way humans are to apes, say. They

aren't close cousins, sharing a family resemblance.
Pterosaurs are reptiles, bats are mammals and birds
and insects are (*checks his notes*) ... birds and insects.
FOUR DIFFERENT ANIMAL FAMILIES, BUT THEY ALL DEVELOPED THE
ABILITY TO FLY, BECAUSE FLYING WORKS IN OUR ATMOSPHERE.

Similarly, we are blessed on Earth with **BRIGHT
SUNSHINE AND CLEAR AIR**. It's probably not
surprising therefore that eyes evolved as many as
forty different times across different families
of animals. Eyes are just useful things to have, here
on Earth.

TALKING WITHOUT WORDS

If life develops on a gas giant planet where thick clouds mean sunlight doesn't penetrate, eyes might not be as necessary. Maybe we'll go to an alien planet, land our ship, walk out into thick cloud and wonder where everyone is. Meanwhile, the locals will have developed a different way of communicating and "seeing" where they are going. Maybe they will use sound, like the way bats use **ECHOLOCATION** to "see" their way in the dark. Bats aren't blind, but in darkness they send out "**clicks**" to locate fast-moving insects by listening for the echo of the sound bouncing off the insect. **Dolphins and whales also use echolocation to locate fish and navigate in water.**

So we should probably send bats and dolphins to distant planets and then they can just report back to us about what they find. **Except that bats and dolphins famously don't get on, because their clicks are slightly different and get on each other's nerves and they would fight the entire way there, like families on a long car journey. Bats are the irritating little brother of the animal world.**

Luckily, we stole all their best ideas. The human versions of echolocation include **radar**, which is a detection system that sends radio waves through air, used for locating aeroplanes, and **SONAR**, which does a similar thing with **sound waves** passing through water, for ships and submarines. We could probably rig up something for astronauts.

MAYBE ALIENS COULD USE ELECTRICITY TO SEE THEIR WAY AROUND, LIKE SHARKS DO.

Some animals use electrolocation, sensing small changes in the electric fields around them. Dolphins can do this, as if they weren't talented enough, but also in a fairly random list, so can bees and the Australian duck-billed platypus. **This would be a weird superhero group.**

Some animals (like the **bluntnose knifefish** in South America) even communicate using **electrocommunication**, sending out a charge to warn off other animals, or attract a mate. **MAYBE THAT SKILL WOULD BE VERY COMMON ON AN ALIEN PLANET**. If it was, we might be unable to join the conversation, or at least find it a challenge, a little like being blind or deaf to human communication here.

There is a chance that the life we find would have no idea what space even was, either because their planet has **thick clouds** or, like the best candidates in the Solar System, Europa (a moon of Jupiter) and Enceladus (a moon of Saturn), which are both huge oceans surrounded by an icy shell, life could exist in an **UPSIDE-DOWN WORLD**, where you would be kept pressed upwards to the "ground" (the inside of the icy shell) because of your own buoyancy. **Creatures on those moons might not even suspect that an entire Universe lay outside their world.**

SUPERHERO STRENGTH AND SPACE FLU

Visiting another planet might be a quick way to become a superhero too. If the planet is smaller, or less dense, than Earth, then it will have **LESS GRAVITY**, and the people there will have evolved to operate in that lower gravity. We will arrive from our **HEAVIER PLANET** with our big muscles and tougher skeletons,

suddenly liberated from the downward pull and free to leap small buildings in a single bound. If we went to Mars, for example, we'd be visiting a planet with only **thirty-eight per cent of our gravity**.

This works both ways, though, and many of the exoplanets we've discovered so far have been "**SUPER EARTHS**": huger versions of our planet. We might arrive and be immediately exhausted from the effort of standing up, on a planet maybe eight times larger than this one. The locals there might be **massively stronger** than us, but mainly perplexed as to why we travelled so far, only to flop around exhausted when we got there. It would certainly calm any urge to pick a fight with our hosts.

Also, the danger from those **giant, super-strong aliens** might not be as serious as the danger from the aliens we **COULDN'T SEE**. Life develops from the very small and eventually, hopefully, up to the very big. The very small doesn't go away though. Fifteen per cent of the weight of all living things on this planet is microscopic bacteria.

We've had **four billion years** of living alongside bacteria and viruses, and still they can turn our world upside down with a few mutations. Imagine an entire planet where all the microbes were totally new. **OUR IMMUNE SYSTEM WOULD FACE CONSTANT ATTACK.**

No wonder when astronauts came back from the Moon, their first stop was quarantine, just in case they had picked up some kind of **SPACE FLU**. When Neil Armstrong, Buzz Aldrin and Michael Collins, the crew of **Apollo 11**, were lifted out of the ocean where they landed, they were whisked past cheering crowds and into quarantine quarters where they stayed for **THREE WEEKS**, longer than they had even spent flying to the Moon and back. And this was after visiting the Moon, which is about as dead a place as you can imagine, apart from the poo they left behind.

Finding Common Ground

But, as I said, the greatest problem might be simply talking to aliens. We have attempted this before. After the Pioneer mission came the **Viking probes**, launched in 1975. This time included in the probe was a **golden audio record**, like a vinyl record that you play on a turntable with a needle. A needle was included with it along with instructions of how to play it.

Again we hit the problem of how to communicate things like speed and distance and all the things we usually communicate through numbers, to an alien people who, while they probably have numbers, won't have the same ones we do. **We count in columns of tens, hundreds, thousands and so on, because we have ten fingers, and it was natural to start counting in tens.** What if aliens don't have ten fingers? What if they have twelve, or six, or none? All the counting systems would be different and none of our numbers would make sense to them.

WHAT IS SO UNIVERSAL THEN THAT IT CAN REPRESENT A DISTANCE BOTH ON EARTH AND ON KEPLER-458B, A BILLION MILES AWAY?

The height of a cow? The width of a shelf? The radius of a football? Look around and try to think what would be the same everywhere. It's only a few hundred years since we measured things in "hands", after all, on the presumption that everyone had similar-ish sized hands.

TRY THAT WITH ALIENS WHO DON'T HAVE HANDS.

247

In a move to make things a little more straightforward, **the metre was invented in 1791**, and later defined as one-millionth the distance between Paris and the North Pole. At one stage, there was even a "**metre stick**" kept in a museum in Paris that ultimately all rulers had to be defined against. None of this would be any help to the Keplerites, of course, who don't get to Paris very often.

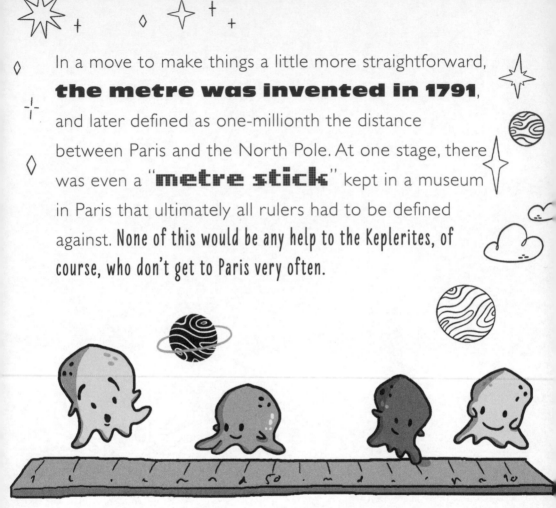

Now a metre has been redefined as "**the distance travelled by light, in a vacuum, in one 299,792,458th of a second**" which is less catchy, but at least is the same anywhere in the Universe, we think. Similarly when the **golden record** was being designed, scientists wanted to find something that would be **THE SAME EVERYWHERE IN THE UNIVERSE** and they chose the most common "thing" in the Universe: **A HYDROGEN ATOM**.

Hydrogen atoms have one proton in the middle, and one electron floating around outside. Do you remember how we spoke about electrons absorbing energy and bits being "missing" in a star's light because of it? Well hydrogen does this too. It **ABSORBS ENERGY** of a particular wavelength, not to jump out to a different orbit, but to make its **electron** "flip" around.

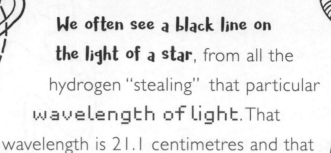

We often see a black line on the light of a star, from all the hydrogen "stealing" that particular **wavelength of light.** That wavelength is 21.1 centimetres and that distance should be fundamental everywhere in the Universe, since hydrogen is everywhere and does the same "**SPINNING DANCE**" everywhere.

On the golden record then, there is a little picture of two hydrogen atoms, one with the electron pointing up, the other with the electron pointing down, and an arrow indicating the distance between them. **Yes, it's a puzzle. I told you, scientists love a puzzle.** They'd love to have some alien scientists to send puzzles to, as well.

So presuming these aliens manage to grab the *Viking* probe as it **ZOOMS PAST**, they then solve the puzzle, work out the 21.1 centimetre length, build the record player and start spinning it at the right speed;

WHAT'S ACTUALLY ON THE RECORD?

Their prize is a series of encoded photos of Earth, showing many facets of life on this planet, as well as illustrating DNA, childbirth, animals of Earth and images of the planet from space. After the photos, there are recordings of sounds from Earth and snippets of music from different cultures around the world. Finally the record ends with greetings in **FIFTY-FIVE DIFFERENT** languages from around the globe. In English the greeting is by the six-year-old son of the scientist, Carl Sagan, who organized the record. His message is, "Hello, from all the children of Earth."

Would an alien culture understand any of this? Will it all sound the same to them? **Probably not and possibly yes, but the better question might be: if we received a similar message what would our reaction be?** We wouldn't have to understand the recording for it to be the most exciting thing ever.

CROSS-SPECIES COMMUNICATION

It's nice to think that we'd eventually crack the language barrier with an alien race, but we have one really obvious reason not to feel too confident. We've been trying to communicate with "alien" intelligences for years, here on Earth, and we've had limited success.

Apes are a pretty close relation to us, and we've been trying to find a common language with them for a long time. A **gorilla called Koko**, living in California, was able to learn **2,000 words of spoken English** and **1,000 SYMBOLS** over the course of her life. Gorillas can't speak, obviously, so a breakthrough came with teaching her a **simple sign language**, based on the sign language that some deaf people use. Koko could use that to make jokes, insult her human companions ("you nut" she would say, or "you bird" - being called a bird is a big insult to a gorilla, seemingly, so remember that next time you're arguing with a gorilla over the last bananas in the supermarket). She could express sadness and communicate if she thought another animal was sad.

At one stage she asked for a **KITTEN** and when she was given a toy kitten instead of a real one, Koko made the symbol for "**sad**" until eventually she was given an actual kitten to care for, who she called **ALL BALL**. She was described as being very gentle and doting with the kitten. Unfortunately, All Ball was killed by a car a year later and when Koko's keepers told her the news, she made the signs for "**BAD, SAD, BAD**" and "**FROWN, CRY, FROWN, SAD, TROUBLE**".

Scientists have also made progress with finding common language with chimpanzees and bonobos, our closest cousins. Kanzi, who lived in the Ape Cognition and Conservation Initiative in Iowa, United States, was said to have reached the communication skills of a three-year-old human. His keepers also believed that they could understand between sixty and eighty bonobo gestures as well, although that probably made them as smart as bonobo three-year-olds in return.

Beyond the primates, **dolphins are pretty smart**. They are the only animal we know that call each other by name. They can arrange themselves into groups and co-ordinate tactics to hunt, and they use tools, which for a long time we thought was a skill only humans had. A very clever scientist called **DENISE HERZING** has worked with a pod of Atlantic spotted dolphins for twenty-eight years, recording their speech and trying to find ways of communicating.

Over time, the dolphins displayed curiosity about their human visitors, **mimicking** their voices and postures and inviting them to join in their games. Herzing even built an **underwater keyboard** for the dolphins, so that they could request their favourite toy. She believes that they can eventually give each human team member a "DOLPHIN NICKNAME", a sound unique to them, that the dolphins will mimic, and use to request specific humans to play with. So, this means that soon, there will be a scientist who is the dolphins' favourite; and that is the greatest achievement ever.

Herzing wants to develop a wearable version of this keyboard, called **CHAT** (it stands for Cetacean Hearing and Telemetry – cetacean is the name for the family of animals that dolphins are in) and this will enable them to communicate both ways – sending whistles the dolphins understand and translating their replies. It will be like wearing a scuba suit with a dolphin translator built in.

Sadly, the chance of us travelling halfway across the **Universe** and then finding a planet full of chimpanzees and playful dolphins is pretty SLIM. It's far more likely to be something completely foreign and different, but smart, like an **OCTOPUS**. Octopuses can shoot ink, camouflage themselves and are famous for taking apart anything they can get their "hands" on. In the **Santa Monica Aquarium** in California, two octopuses once spent the night taking apart the water-recycling system, and when workers came in the next morning they had flooded the building with 750 litres of water. Octopuses are so smart that once, in Brighton Aquarium, one of them left its tank, travelled across the room, climbed into another fish tank, ate the fish, slid back to its own tank and – this is the best bit! – closed the roof on its tank as if it had never left.

I mean, it's **BRILLIANT**, but I bet you're nervously glancing over your shoulder right now, wondering if there's a **sneaky octopus** on the move.

So much work has already been done trying to communicate with different intelligences and we have only had FLEETING GLANCES of what's really going on inside their brains. We don't know if they have any "culture" as such — music or stories, say. We don't know if they **accumulate knowledge** like humans do, or if their "speech" can communicate what human speech can. We certainly don't think they would recognize the wavelength of hydrogen or that they could build a record player. This may be what we end up doing with aliens: marvelling at how amazing they are, while having no earthly idea of how to talk to them.

Still, a planet full of octopuses? That would be worth making a long journey for, right?

SO, WHAT NOW?

HMMM...

I suppose it might seem that this is not a hopeful ending to this book. I mean that octopus story is great, but still, the message generally hasn't been massively positive.

We don't think there's much life in our **Solar System**. We don't think any life we find will be anywhere nearby, or much fun to spend time with. If we do find life in the Universe, it will be very far away and take a **long, long time** to get to.

And when we do meet **ALIEN LIFEFORMS**, they might not be intelligent. And even if they're intelligent, there's a pretty good chance we might not understand them anyway.

Way back at the start of the book we spoke about the **DRAKE** equation, where you multiplied the big numbers by little numbers to find the chances of meeting alien life. And there are a lot of little numbers. Each one makes the whole question just a little more difficult and a little less encouraging.

BUT...

It's an entire Universe we're talking about here.

The big numbers are very, very, very **big**.

We pointed a **TELESCOPE** at one tiny section of the sky, **LESS THAN HALF A CONSTELLATION** — just the left wing of a swan, really — on the off-chance that there would be planets spinning in just the right way and at just the right angle so we could see them, and we found **thousands** of them. We're still finding them, and we're going to send up two more telescopes to look for even more.

Yes, it would be a **mind-bogglingly difficult journey** to reach another planet. But it would also be the greatest journey humankind has ever undertaken, and for the most incredible reason.

And the **best thing** of all? You're here now. You're living in the only fifty years in 4.5 billion years of Earth's history that the planet had an animal on it smart enough to understand space, smart enough to seek out alien life, smart enough to send out a message they might understand and smart enough to look for a reply.

That's you – you're the smart animal. The smartest the planet has ever seen.

Do you want a **big number** for your big brain?

We now think there is at least one planet around each star.

There are **100 billion stars** in our galaxy. There are **one trillion galaxies** in the observable Universe. That means there are **one billion, trillion stars in the Universe** we can see, and orbiting around them are one billion, trillion planets.

So I can't yet tell you what direction you should **WAVE** in to greet the alien reading a version of this book on its planet, wondering about you. **But I can tell you to wave in every direction.**

In every direction you look, at some distance,
there will be a planet capable of sustaining life.
THE BIG NUMBERS ARE JUST TOO BIG.

So **WAVE** in every direction!

Give a **WINK** to all of the stars.

Tell them you'll **TALK** to them soon.

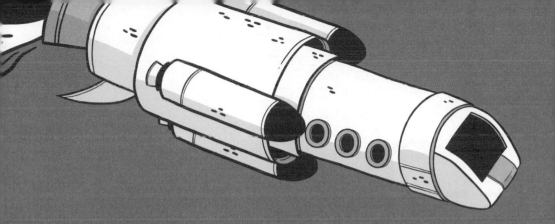

But tell them not to arrive here naked.
That would just be awkward.

About the author

DARA Ó BRIAIN

Dara Ó Briain has a degree in **Mathematics and Mathematical Physics** from University College Dublin. As well as being a **FAMOUS** stand-up **COMEDIAN**, he is one of the BBC's best-known faces of science, presenting such shows as **Dara Ó Briain's Science Club**, flagship astronomy show **Stargazing Live** and DARA Ó BRIAIN: SCHOOL OF HARD SUMS. He lives in London, owns a **TELESCOPE** and has a photo of himself with **Buzz Aldrin**, of which he is **very** PROUD.

Your science notes

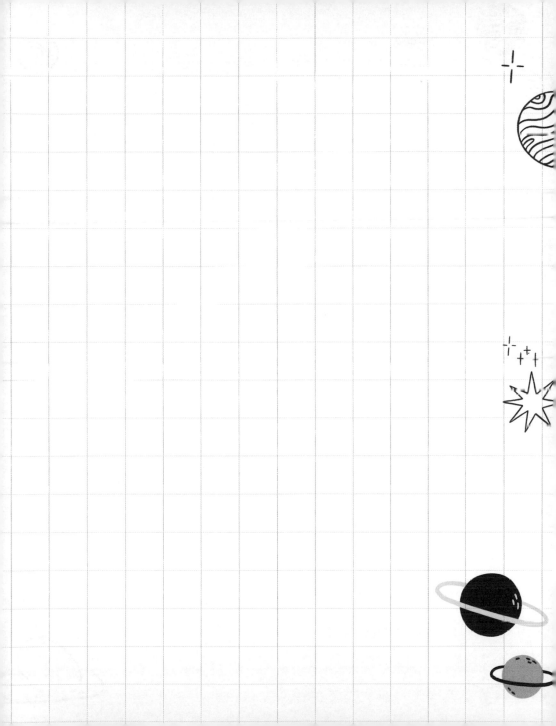

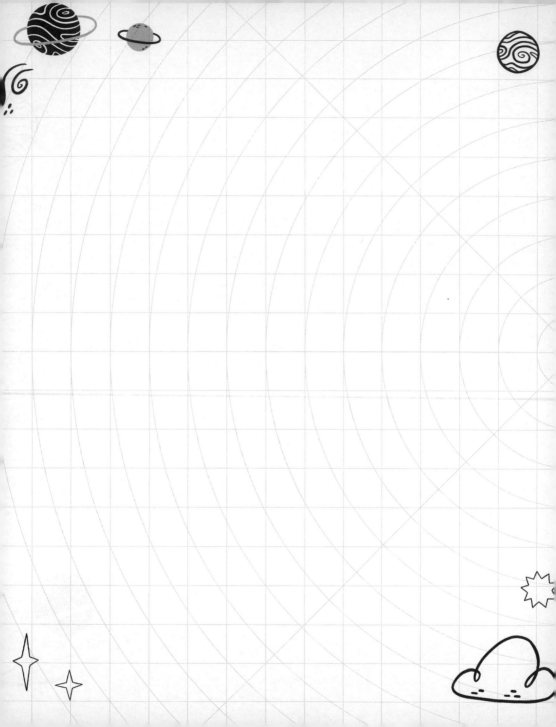

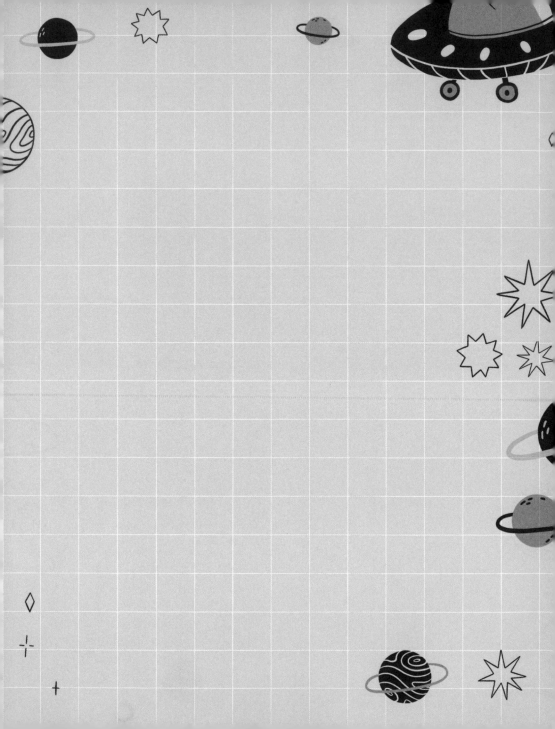

INDEX

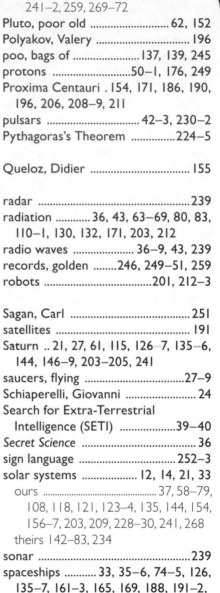